Keys to Reading

MUSTARD SEED MAGIC

Theodore L. Harris
Mildred Creekmore
Margaret H. Greenman

Harold B. Allen
Linguistic Consultant

THE ECONOMY COMPANY
Oklahoma City   Atlanta   Indianapolis

Permission to use or adapt copyrighted material appearing in this book is gratefully
acknowledged on pages 255 and 256, which are hereby made a part of this copyright
page.

ISBN 0–87892–935–5

Contents

People Magic

A Jingle of Coins

River Watch

A City Is People

Snakes Alive

Fe-Fi-Fo-Fum

PEOPLE MAGIC

fringe   fences   chance

Prince

pay   someday   tray

gray

mild   finding   blind

Childs

bush   pushes   bushel

pulled

bench   sniffed   stepped

Mack

balls   walker   walls

hall

seldom   happens   problem

Shelton

thunder   paper   ladder

command

heel

Randy

Part-Time Dog

Randy Shelton stepped off the school bus and walked over to the stoop in front of his apartment house. He sat down on an old bench. It would be a long time before his mother would be home from work. Randy was in no hurry to go upstairs and just play by himself.

"If only I had a dog," thought Randy. "I could take him to the park and have fun. But dogs can't live in this apartment."

Slowly Randy got up and went inside the door. Then he saw a note on the wall by the mailboxes.

WANTED:
A BOY
TO WALK
A DOG.
—
COME TO
759
PARK ST.

Randy read the note three times. A big grin spread across his face. He was a boy! He lived by the park! Walking a dog would be next best to having one!

"Wait until I tell Mom about this!" Randy said to himself. He ran up the stairs two at a time.

Randy was waiting by the door when his mother got home. "There's a note down by the mailboxes," he said. "Someone who lives by the park wants a boy to walk a dog. Let me try to get the job."

"Now just slow down," said Mom, frowning. "Walking a dog is a big job, and something could go wrong."

"But I like dogs," Randy said. "I won't let anything happen."

Randy's mother followed him down to the mailboxes. She read the note. "There's only one way to find out about the job. Talk to the people who live at 759 Park Street," she said. "Then come back and tell me what they say before you take the job."

Randy jumped off the stoop and ran across the park. He found the house and knocked on the door. A woman opened the door.

"I'm Randy Shelton," said Randy. "I saw your note about walking a dog."

"Come in," said the woman. "I'm Mrs. Childs, the housekeeper. Sit down on the bench. Mr. Mack is talking to an older boy." Then she slipped out of the room.

After a while a big boy came up the hall. "The old man said for you to come on in," the boy snapped. "He has a big, mean dog, if you ask me!" Then the big boy ran across the room and out the door.

Randy started down the long, dark hall. Something was pounding inside him. "How big? How mean?" thought Randy.

"Come in!" called a man in a wheelchair. "I'm Mr. Mack. And here's Prince."

"Hi, Prince," said Randy. He patted the dog's head and rubbed him behind the ears. Prince wagged his tail and sniffed Randy's hand.

Mr. Mack smiled. "Now that you and Prince have met, tell me about yourself."

"My name is Randy Shelton, sir," said Randy. "I came to see about walking your dog. I can't have a dog. So walking Prince would be next best to having one."

"I wish I could walk Prince myself," said Mr. Mack, frowning. "But I can't walk him, now that I'm in a wheelchair. Mrs. Childs, my housekeeper, doesn't stay here all day. That's why I need help."

Randy nodded.

"I see Prince likes you better than the other boy," Mr. Mack said. "But that boy was bigger than you. Prince is a very big, strong dog. If he should get away from you, the dogcatcher could get him."

"I'm bigger than I look," Randy said. He stood as tall as he could. "I won't let the dogcatcher get Prince."

"Why not take him for a short walk and see how it goes," said Mr. Mack. "But you must remember each command. *Heel* means walk close behind you. *Sit* means sit down. *Stay* means stop. Do you think you understand each command, Randy?"

Randy nodded. "Yes, sir."

Mr. Mack snapped on Prince's leash and gave it to Randy. "Good luck!" he said.

Out on the sidewalk, Randy tried each command. And Prince followed every command quickly. Then they started down the street. All went well until Prince saw a gray cat crouched on a can. He pulled hard on his leash, and his hair stood up along his back.

Again Randy felt a pounding inside him. His mouth was dry. No words came.

The big, gray cat sat very still on top of the can. Randy pulled hard on the leash, but Prince went on and sniffed at the cat. Again Randy pulled at the leash.

Then at last Randy thought of the right command. "Heel!" he called.

Prince sniffed again. Then he fell in behind Randy. "Good dog!" Randy said. And soon they were back at 759 Park Street.

"Both Prince and I like you," Mr. Mack said. "Why don't you try the job?"

"Thank you!" said Randy. "But I have to talk to my mother first."

Mr. Mack nodded. "I'll be waiting."

Randy almost flew home. "Mom! Mom! I walked the dog!" he called as soon as he stepped inside. "He liked me, and he followed every command I gave him!"

His mother laughed. "That's great! I'm so glad you walked the dog. The job sounds just fine!"

Randy smiled. Even a part-time dog was better than no dog at all!

drink   draw   drug   drugstore

shaking   closed   lined   joking

step   worst   stack   instant

fresh   frowned   fright   fruit

cookie   Connie   brownie   Herbie

queen   question   quite   quart

fastest   wildest   thinnest   tallest

problem   pretty   protect   prettiest

Topolus

Instant Watermelon

15

Herbie sat at the table eating a plum and thinking of Mr. Topolus, who ran the fruit stand. Mr. Topolus was a good friend to children. Sometimes he gave away fruit. Once he gave away some watermelon. That was best of all.

Just thinking about the fruit stand made Herbie hungry for watermelon. He watched his dad fix a drink of instant coffee.

Then Herbie asked, "Why doesn't someone make instant watermelon? Dad, you work in a drugstore. Could you make a pill that would become instant watermelon when you put it in water?"

"I have never thought of that," answered Dad. He began to drink his coffee. "If I have time today, I'll work on an instant watermelon pill."

Then Dad laughed as he left the table, so Herbie thought he might be joking. But that day Dad came home with two big brown bags and one little white bag. He gave the white bag to Herbie. Inside was a bottle with two green pills. Each one looked like a little football. Herbie found a note in the bag.

SMITH DRUGSTORES

Shake and shake a pill so green
Into a tub that's squeaky clean.
Add some water, a quart is plenty.
Run to the stoop, count to 20.

Herbie laughed. "Oh boy!" he shouted. "Can we try the pill right now, Dad?"

"Bring the bottle into the bathroom," said Dad. Then he dropped one of the pills into the bathtub, and he added a quart of cold water.

"Run out on the stoop, Herbie, and count to 20," Dad said. "Come back in when you get to 20, and then we'll know just how well my new pill works."

Herbie thought Dad might be joking. But what if he wasn't? Herbie ran out to the stoop and began to count.

He counted to 20 and ran back into the bathroom. The water was gone. So was the pill. But there in the bathtub was a big, green watermelon! Was it a joke?

Dad cut into the watermelon. Herbie could tell right away that it was a real watermelon!

Herbie ran up and down the street calling all the neighbors. He wanted them to see his instant watermelon.

"How did you make a pill turn into a big watermelon?" the neighbors asked.

Dad smiled and said, "Nothing to it!"

So while all the neighbors stood around the bathtub, Herbie dropped in the other pill that looked like a little football. Then he added one quart of cold water.

"Now just come outside with me," called Herbie, "and count to 20. Then you will see our instant watermelon!"

When the neighbors came back, they could not believe their eyes. The water was gone. So was the pill. But there in the middle of the tub was a big watermelon!

"Now we have plenty of watermelon for everyone!" said Dad.

19

The next day Herbie couldn't wait to tell Mr. Topolus about the instant watermelon pills. Mr. Topolus smiled down at Herbie from behind a big pile of shiny red apples. "You make the joke on me, Herbie?" asked Mr. Topolus.

"Oh, no! All of this really happened, Mr. Topolus!" Herbie said.

"You wait here, and I will fix a bag of real magic!" laughed Mr. Topolus. He went behind a stack of boxes and came out with three round brown things in a bag.

"They look like something to eat," said Herbie.

"Oh, no," said Mr. Topolus. "You plant each one in a pot of dirt, give it some water, and place it in the sun. Then one magic morning you will have the tallest, prettiest flowers you ever saw!"

When Herbie got home, his dad was there, and Herbie forgot about the bag. "Do you have some magic pills?" Herbie asked. "Can we make instant watermelon tonight?"

Dad laughed. "Herbie, I thought you knew that was just a big joke," he said. "Those pills were from the drugstore, and I got the watermelons from Mr. Topolus."

Herbie didn't laugh. He looked down at his shoes. "Then Mr. Topolus knew about the pills all the time," he said.

Suddenly Herbie smiled. "That must be why Mr. Topolus gave me the bag of brown things. He said they were *real* magic!"

Herbie went to his room and opened the bag. "These are not instant flowers," he thought. "But I'll put them in a pot. Then some day I'll have the tallest, prettiest flowers you ever saw!"

Think about This:

Why didn't Mr. Topolus tell Herbie about the joke? Tell about each thing you would need to do to start a flower growing.

fresh finish brushes

rushed

cheese inches reach

March

pick tracked ticket

crack

tumble ladder radar

Toby

glove month son

won

ago besides already

belong

order fork cord

sport

loved shined wiring

skated

Dave

Cleo

Two Ways to Win

Toby and Cleo walked along the street carrying their ice skates. There were many things to see. Cleo liked to look in the store windows, and Toby liked to watch the building machines.

"I like this block more than I thought I would," said Cleo. "I thought there would be nothing for us to do but sit around in the apartment. But with the park on our block, we can ice skate!"

"Another thing I like about living here is that Dad has work all the time now," Toby said.

"But I don't feel like we really belong," said Cleo. "So far we don't have any good friends on our block."

"I know," said Toby. "The other kids talk to us. Mr. March is nice to us at the park. But if we could race on Sports Day, maybe we could make some new friends."

Both Toby and Cleo skated every day after school. They wanted to win their races. Toby saw other boys skating. Some of them were good skaters that would be in the race with Toby.

"I hope I can win that race!" Toby said. On Sports Day, Toby and Cleo hurried to the park. Cleo's race was first. When the girls lined up to race, Toby saw one girl much bigger than Cleo.

"Well, that tallest girl will win," Toby thought. "With those long legs, she will be fast. Too bad for Cleo!"

But Cleo got off to a good start. The tall girl could not keep up with her. Then a girl named Sue started to pass all of the skaters. Soon she was just behind Cleo, skating very fast. Suddenly Cleo hit a big crack in the ice and fell. She jumped up quickly and skated hard. But Sue didn't fall, and she won the race.

All the girls were laughing and talking as they rushed over to Sue.

"You did it! You did it!" they shouted over and over again.

Cleo skated away from the girls. Toby came to her and asked, "Did you hurt your leg?"

Cleo shook her head, and she sat down on a bench. "I lost my race," she said. "Now, Toby, you will have to win your race. If you don't win, we won't get to know any new people around here."

It was time for Toby to get ready for his
race. A tall boy named Dave lined up beside
Toby. The race started! Toby skated very
fast, and he was ahead of many of the boys.
He was able to pass everyone but Dave.
Toby could not catch him.

All at once something happened! Dave's
skate hit the same crack in the ice that
Cleo had hit. Down he went!

There was a snap! Toby saw Dave
frowning and holding his leg. Toby stopped
beside Dave. But all the other skaters
rushed by. "Don't get up," Toby said to
Dave. Then he shouted, "Mr. March!
Mr. March!"

Mr. March rushed over. When he saw
Dave's leg, he said, "Maybe you broke a
bone! It's a good thing you didn't get up."

"Toby could have won that race," said
Bill. "But he stopped to help Dave."

"What a good sport!" Tim added.

Then Sue and Carl walked over to Cleo.
"Are you Toby's sister?" Sue asked.

"Yes, I'm Cleo," she answered.

"You're a good skater!" said Sue. "And
your brother is really a good sport!"

Carl nodded. "I hope Toby plays ball. We
will need a good catcher next spring."

When Cleo heard Carl, she thought,
"There is more than one way to win!" And
then she rushed over to tell Toby.

taught   ought   though

whip   whisper   whine

walls   baseball   stalk

ray   driveway   stray   pay

lodge   fringe   badge

Carol   Maria   strange

dough

whispered

Walker

tray

age

they'll

Neighbors

29

A Strange Visit

Carol Walker stood on the top step and looked up and down the street. Today new neighbors would be moving into Jane's house next door.

"There will be a girl your age living in the house," said Mother, "just as before."

"But no one can take Jane's place," said Carol. "She was my best friend!"

Just then a car turned into the driveway next door and stopped. "There's the girl," Carol whispered, "and her mother, too."

30

The girl and her mother left their car. They walked across the driveway and started into their house. Then Carol heard the girl say something to the lady.

"Did you hear that, Mother?" Carol cried. "She didn't speak English!"

"Come inside, Carol. We'll talk about that in the house," whispered Mother.

"But she didn't speak English!" Carol said again when they were inside.

"No, but the girl is about your age, and her mother looks very friendly," Mother said. "They'll be our new neighbors. And I hope they'll be our friends, too. We just need to think of some way to understand each other."

Then Mrs. Walker turned on the oven. She began to make some cookie dough.

"You're going to make cookies for them?" Carol asked.

"Yes, just as I did when Jane and her family moved in," Mrs. Walker said. "You can help by getting a tray ready."

At last the cookie dough was ready to be rolled into little balls. Before long the kitchen was filled with the good smell of cookies, hot from the oven. Carol put some cookies on the tray and went next door. She knocked three times.

The door opened a crack. A small dark face looked out.

"Mother sent these," said Carol as she held out the tray to show the cookies. "We live next door."

The door opened a little more. The girl's hand came out and took the tray.

Then Carol said, "My name is Carol. What is yours?" But the girl just stood there looking at the tray.

"Mother made the cookies," Carol said. Still the girl said nothing. She began to close the door.

Carol ran home. "Mother, you said to be friendly!" she cried. "So I gave the girl the cookies, and I told her my name. She didn't say a thing, and she didn't even let me step inside the house."

"Help me clean up, and I will tell you something I know," said Mother. "Mrs. Land, at school, called this morning. She told me that our neighbors are from another country. They speak Spanish. The mother can say a few English words, but Maria cannot."

"Then how can we ever be friends?" asked Carol. "We can't even talk to each other. And she shut the door in my face."

"Maria did that only because English is strange to her," Mother said. "She didn't know what you were saying. But she will be learning English in school."

"Well, I wish she were more like Jane," said Carol. "Maria is strange."

"You need to think of some things to do together without talking," said Mother. "There are other ways of learning to know each other."

"Maybe we could take Maria and her mother to the zoo," said Carol.

"Yes!" said Mother. "I'll ask them if they'll be able to go."

We work with words.

spare   scare   aware   cared

twist   twice   twenty

planned   tapped   beginning

Sight words.

Sí   Lobo

Sound the words.

scared

twelve

grabbed

understanding

More Than Words

Their trip to the zoo got off to a bad start. Carol and Maria walked along slowly, without talking. Their mothers talked, but the girls said nothing.

"I don't know why I thought coming here would help," Carol said to herself. "We can't even talk to each other!"

Carol looked at Maria. She was looking around, but she didn't smile.

"If only I could help," Carol thought. "How would I feel if I were in a strange country?"

Suddenly Carol stopped. Her face lit up. She tapped on the sign by a cage. Then she pointed to the animal inside.

"Wolf!" said Carol. She smiled at Maria and said, "Wolf!"

Maria smiled. Then Maria tapped on the sign and said, "Wolf." She pointed to the animal in the cage and said, "Wolf."

Then Maria shouted out, *"Lobo!"* And she pointed to the wolf.

"Lobo!" Carol shouted right back.

Carol and Maria looked at each other and began to laugh. Carol grabbed Maria's hand, and the two girls ran ahead to the big bear cage.

When they saw the brown bear standing on his back legs, Carol jumped to the side as if she were scared.

At the next cage, Maria jumped back to show Carol she was scared of the red fox crouched in the corner. They didn't need words to understand each other.

It was Maria who pointed out the possum babies. Then Maria held up her hand. But Carol shook her head to show she didn't understand.

Again Maria pointed to the babies. She put Carol's hand in hers. Then she tapped until she counted to twelve.

"Oh!" Carol jumped up and down. "I know. You're saying I could put the twelve little babies in my hand!"

Maria's mother walked up behind the girls. *"Sí! Sí!"* she said. "Maria knows about many animals!"

Mrs. Walker put her arm around Carol. "I see you're finding ways of understanding each other without talking. Soon you'll be good friends."

Carol nodded and grabbed Maria's hand. "Come on, Maria. I know something else you will like—hot dogs!"

Think about This:

How could you tell about a zoo animal without saying words?

What would you do if you lived where no one could speak English?

scrub	scream	scrape	scratch
		survey	obey
I've	we've	they've	you've
ginger	barges	gypsy	message
sale	vote	snake	wave

Messages without Words

Did you ever get a message without words?

When you came to school today, did the look on someone's face say, "I'm happy!"

If you ever got mud on the floor, what was the message on your mother's face?

If a baseball goes past the catcher, he may scratch his head as he looks for it. Do you understand his message?

Did you ever think of a smile or a frown or a scratch as a message?

Many times the way someone moves sends a message. When you see a boy running, he seems to say, "I'm in a hurry."

You've seen the boys on a baseball team jump up and down when the game is over. Did you get a message from that? The way they moved seemed to say, "Our team won!"

What messages do you get when you see your friends wave to you?

There are so many ways to send messages without words.

A wave of the hand can mean "Hello!" A policeman does not have to say anything when he sends the message, "Stop!" He can hold up his hand, and you will obey. Yes, you do get his message! The lady at the library may send you a message by putting her hand over her mouth. Do you get the message? Will you obey?

Now tell about some other ways you've seen messages sent without words.

collect   supper   letter

brownie   Freddie   Ronnie

guard   guided   guesses

July   bicycle   gypsy

shined   shaking   waved

ladder

Connie

guessed

mystery

giving

answer

Mystery of the Moving Snowman

43

Everyone on the block was trying to find an answer to the mystery of the big, moving snowman. In the daytime this tall snowman stood very still. But at night he moved from yard to yard.

How did that tall snowman move around? That was the mystery! The Downtown Club was giving a sled to the boy or girl who found the answer to the mystery.

One cold morning Tim came inside calling to his sister, Connie. "Look, the snowman is on our driveway today! If we can guess how he got there, we'll win the sled."

44

"We'll have the first guess today," said Connie, "because he's at our house."

"Come on out, and let's take a good look at him," Tim called from the front door.

Connie ran outside with her brother. She looked at the snowman and shouted, "He's the tallest man in town! And he's as fat as an elephant!"

"Let's look for tracks first," said Tim. But there were no tracks in the snow.

"Maybe he flew over," said Connie. "No one has guessed that."

"Denny guessed that he had wheels under him and that someone pulled him along," said Tim. "But that's not right."

"I still think he flew up the street," said Connie. She laughed as she thought of a big snowman flying in the sky.

Tim didn't feel like joking. He knew that a right guess was the only way he could get a sled. He wanted to find the answer to the mystery and win that sled!

"We know he can't move by himself," said Tim. "Someone has to move him. How could they do it?"

"Maybe he gets help from a plane or a helicopter," Connie said.

"That might be the answer!" Tim said. "But how could a helicopter pick him up?"

"A man could climb down a rope ladder and tie another rope around the snowman," said Connie. "Then the helicopter could fly him up the street."

"Where would they tie the rope?" asked Tim. "The snowman would fall apart."

Connie and Tim walked around the snowman. Connie stopped to look at the brown mop on top of his head.

"I keep thinking about that funny hair," said Connie. "Have you ever seen a snowman with hair like that?"

"No. Maybe there's something under it," said Tim. "I'll get a ladder and see."

Connie held the ladder, and Tim climbed up. He felt around under the brown mop. "It's here!" he shouted. "A big ring! And a hook could go into this ring!"

"A helicopter could do it," said Connie.

"Maybe," Tim said. "But we never see or hear one around here."

"And our street has too many buildings for a helicopter to land," Connie added.

"That's right," Tim said. "Why don't we go inside and think about it some more."

47

Tim and Connie thought and thought and talked and talked. After a while Connie gave up and began looking at a book.

Suddenly she shouted, "Look! Here's a big crane with a hook. It could lift anything. Why couldn't it lift our snowman?"

"It could!" cried Tim. "A crane could lift a big snowman and put him down anywhere."

"But who has a crane around here?" asked Connie.

"I saw a crane near the Downtown Club," said Tim. "I think they are putting up a new building."

"Let's hurry and write a letter giving our answer," Connie cried. "I just know the crane is the right answer!"

"Help me write the letter," said Tim.

After they wrote the letter, they took it to the Downtown Club. As Mr. Horn read their letter, he smiled.

"You guessed right! The sled is yours," said Mr. Horn as he shook hands with Tim and Connie. "The snowman can stay at your house, too. The moving snowman will not be moving again!"

49

A jingle of coins

young   trouble   rough

dial   poem   Indian

weigh   freight   sleigh

baker   visitor   collar

harm   radar   tardy

enough

idea

eight

dollars

Hardy

against

David

librarian   special   build

Too Many Books

After school David grabbed his lunch box and hurried down the hall. His mother was the town librarian, and he always met her at the library after school. The library was a special place in town. People came there to visit as well as to get books.

It was snowing outside, and big dots of snow lit on David's cap as he ran up the hill to the library. His mother smiled when he stepped up to her desk. "Pick out a book and sit on that bench while you're waiting," she whispered. "If it keeps snowing, we'll close the library."

So David sat down close to the fireplace, watching the people. He was proud that his mother was the librarian!

At home that night, David could hear the library bell ring and the loud roar of a fire truck. He ran to the bedroom window, looking for some sign of a fire. At the top of the high hill, flashes of light splashed against the dark sky. "Mother!" shouted David. "The library is on fire!"

Mother ran to the window in time to see the library roof tumble down. She cried, "Oh, David! The library is gone."

The town seemed very strange without a library. It would take plenty of money to build a new one. No one knew what to do, but many people tried to help get money for a new library.

In the spring some mothers held a cake sale. They made twelve dollars at the sale, but that wasn't enough money to start a new library.

Then David and his friends put on a show in an old empty school building. They made more than eight dollars. But that wasn't enough money.

People asked David's mother to start a part-time library. But they couldn't find enough books or space for even a part-time library. Everyone was upset, and no one knew what to do.

One Saturday morning David said to his mother, "I'm going to ask people to give us books for the library. I'll tie my wagon onto my bike. Maybe people will fill the wagon with books."

"That's a good idea," said Mother. "We need all the books you can get. I'll fix some lunch for you, and you can eat it on the way."

By lunchtime David had twelve books.
"Twelve isn't enough," David thought.
"I'll ask for more books after lunch."

Just then David heard a band playing. He
rode to the bandstand. There he saw Mayor
Hardy with the band. A sign read VOTE
FOR MAYOR HARDY AGAIN.

David ate lunch while the band played.
Mayor Hardy asked the people to vote for
him. Then he left the bandstand and walked
over to David.

"You have some nice books," the mayor
said. "Are they for something special?"

"Yes, these books are for the library,"
David said. "But we need more books."

"I have an idea," said the mayor. "I'm going to be giving a talk on TV this very afternoon. Why don't you come along and talk about the library?"

"That's a great idea!" said David. "I could ask people to help us build a new library."

"And it seems to me they'll want to give books, too," said Mayor Hardy.

After the TV show David came home in a long, shiny car. His friends were surprised to see him tumble out of the car and wave good-by to the mayor.

After that day, David's mother always seemed to be stacking books. "Eight trucks filled with books came today," she sighed. "Now we have too many books!"

David looked around. There were books stacked against the wall, books on the big table, and books on David's bed.

"We are having a meeting today at the old school to talk about a library," said his mother. "We must find a place for these books!"

"That's it!" cried David. "The old school is empty, Mother! What a good place to put books!"

"You're right, David!" said Mother. "We can have a library there."

Everyone at the meeting liked the idea of making the school into a library. What a hustle and bustle! Mothers came to clean, and fathers came to paint. And boys and girls helped carry books.

At last came the very special day. David woke up to the clang of the library bell. The new library was open! Later the band played while people walked around to see all the books. Mayor Hardy brought a gold sign for the front of the building. The people cheered.

David walked inside to look at all the books lined up along the wall. His mother smiled at him from behind her desk.

"You know, a library really can't have too many books!" said David.

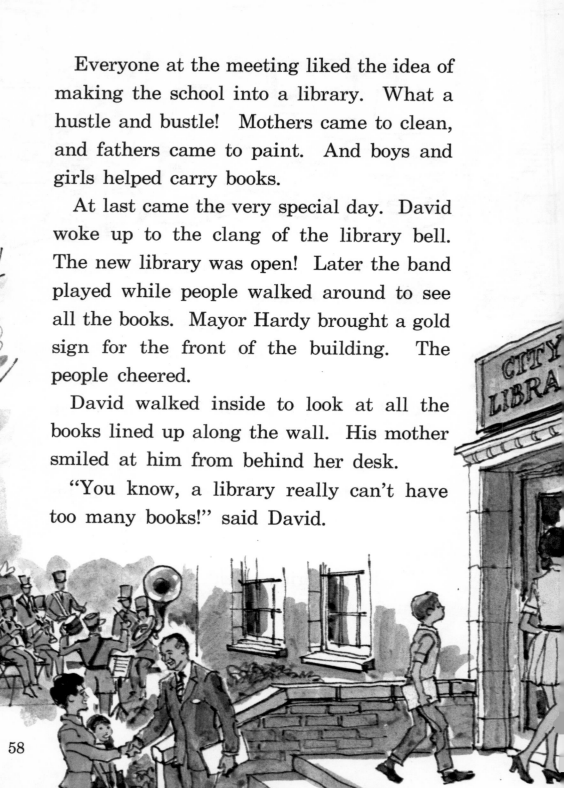

glasses	cities	pushes	brushes
frost	cloth	toss	cloths
they've	we've		I've
spear	pear	earn	earned
chased	wiring	closed	shined
supper	vacation	number	polish
fuel	violet	meow	radio
			shoeshine
			New York
			hardware

Shoeshine Boy

Rat-a-tat-tat!

Teddy lived in New York City. He went to school in the winter, and in the summer he played out of doors. It was fun when the ice-cream bell rang, but Teddy's mother could not give him money every day.

"Why don't you get a job?" his brother George asked. "I earned money when I was your age."

A job! That was a fine idea. Teddy saw a sign Boy Wanted in the cleaning shop.

"No," Mr. Brown said. "You couldn't carry these without dragging them on the floor."

"A job?" said Mr. Stone at the hardware store. "Some of my orders have to be carried up many stairs. You couldn't do that. They are too heavy."

Teddy saw a boy named Roy eating ice cream. He knew that Roy shined shoes. "How do you get to be a shoeshine boy?" he asked Roy.

"Oh, it's easy," Roy answered. "You fix up a box like this. You get brushes and polish and cloths for brown and black shoes. Then you find yourself a good spot where lots of people go by."

"Where do you get those things?" Teddy asked.

"At the hardware store," Roy answered. "And you have to call out like this, 'Shine, shine, who wants a shine?' Sir, do you want a shine?" Roy called to a man.

"Yes, I need one," the man said.

Teddy watched Roy put cleaning polish on with a little round brush. He rubbed it with a cloth and then put hard polish on. Rat-a-tat-tat! The cloth made a happy sound as Roy rubbed it against the man's shoes. More polish, a big brush, and then the shoes were shined!

"That's a good shine," the man said when both shoes were done. "And here's a nickel for a tip."

"I think I could do that," Teddy said. But how was he going to get the things he needed?

"I'll give you the money, and you can pay me back later," George said.

Teddy went to the hardware store, and Mr. Stone helped him put his things together.

Then Teddy started out for work. "Shine, shine, who wants a shine?"

Two feet stopped in front of him. They did not need a shine. "Move on," said the policeman.

Teddy walked and walked, and then he
came to Radio City. "Shine, shine, who
wants a shine?"

"You can't shine shoes in Radio City,"
a guard said.

"But I'm chased away from everywhere,"
Teddy moaned.

"Why don't you go over near the library?"
the guard said. "I've seen lots of shoeshine
boys there."

angry   jingled   twinkle   twinkled

nation   question   lotion   attention

fastest   hottest   widest   littlest

milkman   sunfish   eggshells   anyone

supermarket

Who Wants a Shine?

Shine—want a shine—shine up, sir—ten cents a shine!"

Teddy saw Roy waving to him. He slipped into a place next to Roy. "Shine—shine!" Teddy called out. A man stopped, but not at his box.

"Shine—shine!" Teddy saw lots of men stop, but never at his box. He couldn't get anyone to pay attention to him.

"Why doesn't anyone pay attention to me?" Teddy asked Roy.

One of the boys heard Teddy. "No one wants a shine from a little kid like you."

"You're the littlest shoeshine boy here," Roy said.

And then a boy bigger than Teddy or Roy came along. "Go on! Beat it!" he said to Teddy. "I want this place."

Poor Teddy! He didn't know where to go. His box felt so heavy that he began to walk home. He passed the hardware store and came to the supermarket.

"What's that box for?" a boy asked.

"It's a shoeshine box," Teddy answered.

"Oh, will you shine my cowboy boots?" the boy asked.

"Shine your boots? You're just a little kid." Then Teddy remembered that he had not liked being called that. "All right, I'll give you a shine," he said.

Teddy put cleaning polish on with the little round brush. He rubbed it with a cloth and put hard polish on. Rat-a-tat-tat! went his cloth. Soon the boots twinkled!

"Billy, what are you up to?" said a lady who came out of the supermarket. Then she saw Teddy. "How nice! I haven't had time to clean Billy's boots. How much do I owe you?"

"Owe me?" Teddy looked at the shine. "Would five cents be all right?"

"That would be fine," the lady said.

And then Teddy suddenly had an idea!

The next morning Teddy was back at the supermarket. "Shine! Shine your children's shoes for only five cents!"

A mother with a little girl came by.

"What a good idea! You can shine Anna's shoes while I shop."

Rat-a-tat-tat! Soon Anna's shoes twinkled like new. Her mother gave Teddy five cents for a tip.

"Shine! Shine your children's shoes!" he called. Teddy shined shoes all day long.

Teddy shined shoes in front of the same
supermarket all summer. He earned enough
money to pay back his brother. He earned
enough to get ice cream and other things.

Summer ended. It was time to go back to
school. And Teddy put away his shoeshine
box.

Shoeshine Song

Shine, mister, shine?
Shine your shoe
For only a dime?
I'll clean off your shoe,
I'll slick it up fine—
All for a dime.

Look at your shoe!
I'll tap it and slap it
And rap it and strap it.
I'll make it look new.
For you,
A shiny new shoe
For you.

I'll make your shoe
Look just like new!
All for a dime,
Shine, mister, shine!

by Lois Lenski

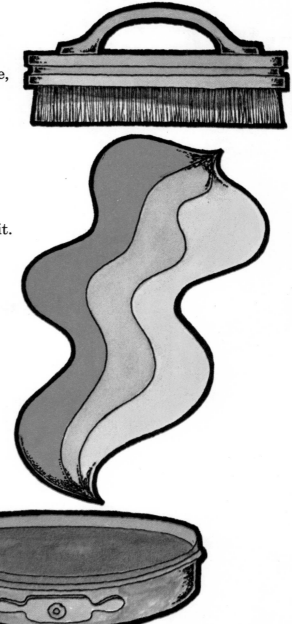

70

repay   return   repair   repairing

vacation   direction   suggestion   question

touch   young   rough   trouble

tardy   patty   angry   Plinsky

war   warmer   warn   warned

bucket   important   happens   electrical

use   cause   sense   cheese

Herbert

electrician   different

Herbert, the Electrician

Don stood at Dad's workbench, repairing Herbert's leash. Herbert, a sleek, white mouse, sat in a cage nearby.

Don was thinking about his dad working at school. Dad was an electrician. While the children were on vacation, he was repairing the wiring at Don's school.

"I wish Dad had taken me along so I could help," thought Don. "It's my school, and I'm on vacation."

Don's dad always said, "You can help when you're a little older, son."

"Older, older, older!" moaned Don. He hooked the leash on Herbert and put him in his pocket.

Just then Don's mother came to the door with a lunch box in her hand. "Dad forgot his lunch this morning," said Mother. "Will you take it to him?"

"Sure! But let me ask a question," said Don. "Can I stay awhile with Dad?"

"Yes, if Dad says so," said Mother. "But don't get in his way."

Don hurried to school with Herbert in his pocket and the lunch box under his arm. He found Dad and Mr. Plinsky, the floorman, in the basement.

Don watched as his dad tried to push a wire through a long, dark hole in the wall. "No luck!" said Dad. Mr. Plinsky frowned and shook his head.

73

"I brought your lunch, Dad," said Don.

"Oh, thanks, son. Put it over there on the table," said Dad. And he picked up the wire again. "I'll try one more time. If I have to knock out the wall, I can't get this work done before school starts."

Don watched as his dad pushed the wire. "Dad, will you answer a question for me?" Don asked. "Why doesn't that wire go on through to the other end of the hole?"

"It gets stuck in the middle, son," Dad answered.

"And pushing and pounding won't help a blinking bit!" said the floorman in his squeaky voice.

All of the talking woke up Herbert. He stuck his head out of Don's pocket.

"Dad, let's get Herbert to pull the wire through the hole in the wall!" Don said.

"He might get stuck," said Dad.

"We can tie the wire to a string. Then we can tie the string around his neck," said Don. "It should be easy to get him to go through."

"We don't want a blinking mouse living inside our school walls," said Mr. Plinsky.

"Let me try," begged Don. "Herbert is not afraid of a hole, and he will obey me."

Mr. Plinsky looked at Dad. "There will be trouble if that mouse gets stuck in the wall," warned Mr. Plinsky. "But you're the electrician."

"I think we'll try out the mouse," said Dad. "Get Herbert ready, son."

Don took Herbert out of his pocket and tied the string around his neck. Then he put him into the hole in the wall and gave him a little push.

"Go on in, Herbert," Don said.

The mouse went into the hole and then stopped. Don kept pushing him. "Please go!" begged Don. "Obey me!"

But Herbert was very slow about going into the dark hole. Then at last he went inside the hole very slowly, pulling the string after him.

Again Herbert stopped. Don yanked the string. Then he pulled on it, but the sleek little mouse did not move.

"Too bad, son," said Dad. "Your mouse has stopped. Pull him out."

"Come on, Herbert!" begged Don.

"Do you think he's running around in the walls?" asked Mr. Plinsky.

"No, he's taking a nap," Don said.

"I can't wait much longer," warned Dad. It looked like trouble. Poor Don!

"Oh, I knew it wouldn't work," cried Mr. Plinsky. "I've never ever heard of a mouse electrician!"

"Dad, I have an idea!" Don said. "Herbert might come out for some food."

Dad took some cheese from his lunch box. He put it at the other end of the hole. Then Don yanked the string.

Before long the string started moving through Don's hand.

"Herbert is awake!" cried Don. "He has picked up the smell of the cheese."

Mr. Plinsky ran to the end of the hole just as Herbert jumped out with cheese in his mouth. "I never thought I would see an electrical mouse!" he cried.

"That was good thinking, son," said Dad. "After lunch you can help me do the rest of the wiring."

Don smiled as he hooked the little leash on Herbert. "Some day we might have three good electricians at our house," he said.

Think about This:

How did Don feel when Herbert stopped moving? Did Mr. Plinsky seem different at the end of the story?

couple   touch   tough

fair   prairie   chairs

break   sweater   stream

north   important   orbit

roots   wooden   tools

rough

repair

reach

order

hooks

pole

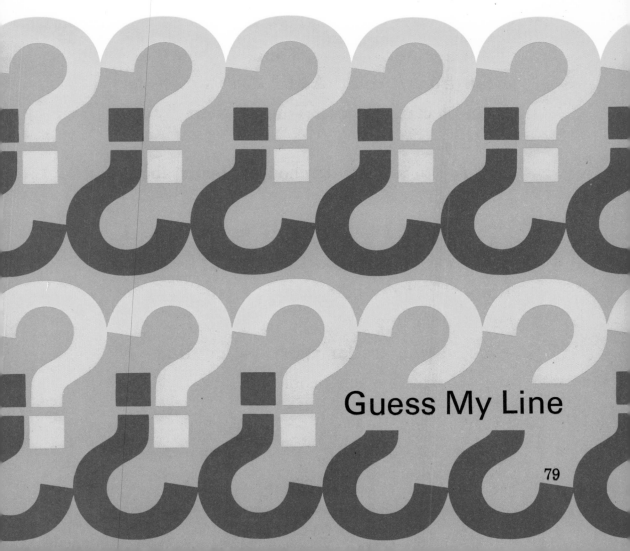

Guess My Line

Do you like to climb things and work outside? If so, you would like my job. I help put in lines for new houses.

Do you like rough work in bad weather? If so, you would like my job. When there is a storm, I look for lines on the ground. These lines might hurt people. I repair any lines that are on the ground or any lines that are out of order.

When I repair lines, I must be sure not to fall from a pole. And I must watch out for an electrical wire. This is when my job is really rough.

I went to a special school to learn about my work.

The clothes I wear help me in my work. I have shoes with hooks on them to help me climb. I put my belt around a pole to keep me from falling.

People who are far apart use my lines in order to reach each other.

What's my line?

We work with words.

finger   ankle   jingle

cities   fried   noisily

replace   repay   refill

hammer   towboat   pilot

point   royal   join

Sight word.

Rosita

Sound the words.

jingled

merrily

return

Gomez

coins

fisherman

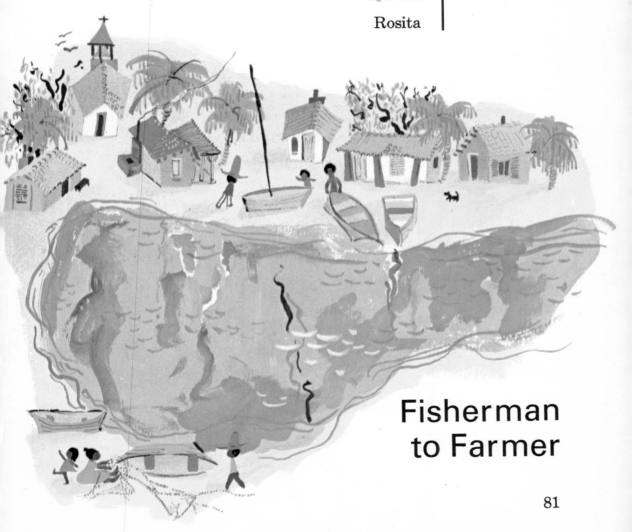

Fisherman to Farmer

81

Rosita Gomez lived near a big lake. Her father was a fisherman.

Each day Mr. Gomez would throw out a big net to catch fish. Rosita would help her father pull in the net and pile the fish in baskets. Then off to market they would go to sell the fish!

One day Mr. Gomez sold the fish quickly. Then he gave Rosita all the money she had earned. How merrily the coins jingled in her pocket!

"Why don't you get something with your money, Rosita?" her father asked.

"I'm saving my money for a pet," said Rosita as she jingled the coins.

Later that summer the lake became dry.
Mr. Gomez and Rosita couldn't go fishing
any more. Now there were no trips to town.
No coins jingled in Rosita's pocket.

"Now I will never have enough money for
a pet," sighed Rosita.

Each night she would lie down on her mat
and wish for the fish to come back to the
lake. But they didn't return. The family
had less and less to eat.

One day a man from the city came to show
each fisherman a new way to earn money.
"I have two baskets of chickens for you,"
said the man. "But don't eat the chickens.
Let them lay eggs."

"Lay eggs!" said Mrs. Gomez. "I want the chickens for our supper!"

"But you can sell their eggs and use the money for other food," said the man.

Mr. Gomez frowned. "People in our town don't eat eggs," he said.

When the man left, Mrs. Gomez took the baskets. "The chickens will make a good supper," she said.

"Will you let me have two chickens for pets?" asked Rosita.

"All right, Rosita," said her mother. "Which hens do you want?"

Rosita took a white hen and a red one. Her father helped her build a house for the chickens. And before long the hens began to lay eggs.

Mrs. Gomez said, "Now we will eat the eggs."

"M-m-m-m. *Sí, sí,*" said Mr. Gomez.

"M-m-m-m. *Sí, sí,*" said Rosita.

And after that the Gomez family ate eggs every day.

But soon they were tired of eggs. Mr. Gomez said so. And Mrs. Gomez said so. But Rosita was afraid to say so. Her mother might cook the two hens.

Rosita thought about this as she lay on her mat one night. "Just how can I get something for us to eat besides eggs?"

After that Rosita saved two eggs each day. And one day when her father went to town, Rosita asked if she could go.

"Why do you want to go to town?" asked Mrs. Gomez.

"I want to surprise you!" said Rosita. "I will tell you when we return."

Rosita put some eggs in a basket. Then she and her father started to town.

On the way to market, Rosita told her father about her plan to earn money.

As soon as they got to town, Rosita cried, "Fresh eggs! Fresh eggs!" And before long, coins jingled merrily in her pocket.

"Now what will I get to surprise Mother?" thought Rosita. "I have to find something everyone will like to eat."

Rosita stopped at the meat store. Right above her head was a beautiful ham. And Rosita had enough money to get some of the ham!

What a supper they had that night!

"Ham and eggs!" said her mother. "Even eggs are good again, with ham!"

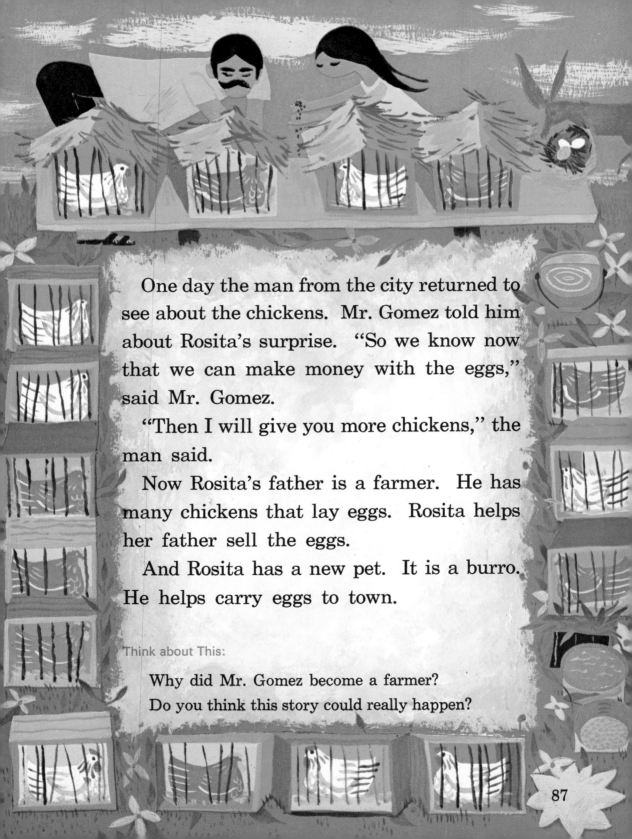

One day the man from the city returned to see about the chickens. Mr. Gomez told him about Rosita's surprise. "So we know now that we can make money with the eggs," said Mr. Gomez.

"Then I will give you more chickens," the man said.

Now Rosita's father is a farmer. He has many chickens that lay eggs. Rosita helps her father sell the eggs.

And Rosita has a new pet. It is a burro. He helps carry eggs to town.

Think about This:

Why did Mr. Gomez become a farmer?
Do you think this story could really happen?

87

river
watch

Ways of the River

89

A river may be little or big. It may be
slow and quiet or fast and fierce. But
rivers are important to people.

All rivers have names. Sometimes the
man who finds a river names it. He may
give it the name of some place or thing. So
our rivers have all kinds of names—Milk
River, Bear River, Yellow River, or
Mississippi River.

Rivers have always helped people in many ways. Before there were highways, a river was the fastest way to take heavy loads from one place to another.

Rivers still help us in many ways. They give us water to drink. They give us a place to fish, swim, and sail boats. And rivers still carry heavy loads.

Animals of the woods come to rivers to drink or to take a bath. And the river is home for many fish and birds.

Sometimes a river will flood the land. Then it brings trouble to people who live close by. Even quiet rivers seem fierce when they flood.

So people have learned to manage rivers. They have put dams across the river bed. They use dams to store water in time of flood. Later people will have water, even when there isn't much rain.

Today we must manage to keep our rivers clean. Then they will always be ready for people and animals to use.

Rivers are still important!

We work with words.

permission   television

group   soupy   croup

digging   clipped   stepping

she's   she'll   they're

worse   workmen   worth

Sight word.

minute

Sound the words.

confusion

route

planned

we've

worm

Oliver

Crummel

Wishing Worms

93

Oliver had been wishing for a nice, warm Saturday like this one. He planned to go fishing with his brother Tom and his friend Mike.

Oliver put on his old clothes and hurried downstairs. He couldn't find Tom. "Did he go fishing without me?" thought Oliver. Then he ran to the basement, where he had put his fishing worms. He looked around in confusion. The fishing worms were gone, too!

"I feel awful!" Oliver thought.

When Oliver felt awful, he always sat on the back steps of his house to think. So he went to the back steps.

Oliver sat thinking for a long time. Soon he thought of something that would make him feel better. He reached inside the door to get his fishing hat. He put on the hat, and he picked up his fishing rod and a bucket. Then he started walking.

First he saw the milkman. Oliver's house was the last stop on the milk route. "Good morning, Oliver. Going fishing?" asked the milkman.

"Not right now," answered Oliver.

Next Oliver met the postman, who was just starting along his mail route. "Are you going fishing today, Oliver?" asked the postman.

"Later on," answered Oliver.

Soon Oliver smelled something good. It led him right to the Crummel Bake Shop. Oliver knew that a Crummel cookie would make him feel better!

When Oliver walked into the bake shop, a bell on the door jingled. Mr. Crummel looked up from his work and smiled.

Oliver put his rod and his bucket on the floor. Then he climbed up on a high stool beside Mr. Crummel.

"Would you be kind enough to try one of my cookies, Oliver?" asked Mr. Crummel.

Oliver ate one of the cookies. "Mmmmm. It's good," he said.

Mr. Crummel said, "That's what I wanted to hear. But you don't look happy today, Oliver. Is something wrong?"

Oliver felt awful again.

"Everything went wrong today!" Oliver moaned. "I had some fishing worms, and I planned to go to the river with Tom and Mike."

"That sounds like a good plan," said Mr. Crummel. "What happened?"

"When I got up this morning, Tom and Mike were gone," said Oliver. "My fishing worms were gone, too. I think Tom and Mike went fishing without me."

"Such confusion!" cried Mr. Crummel. "Why don't you go fishing by yourself?"

"It's too late now to find good fishing worms," said Oliver.

"Well, I'm not so sure about that," said Mr. Crummel. "Did you ever try to catch fish with wishing worms?"

"Wishing worms!" cried Oliver.

"Yes, wishing worms," Mr. Crummel said. "I can make some for you."

Mr. Crummel reached for some dough and rolled it into small white strings. They looked like little worms.

"Let these dry a few minutes," said Mr. Crummel. "Then we'll fill your bucket, and you can go fishing. But you have to make a wish before the fish will bite."

"That must be why you call them wishing worms," said Oliver. Mr. Crummel nodded.

"And remember this, too," Mr. Crummel whispered. "Don't tell any other fisherman about this. Just wish to yourself."

"I'll remember," said Oliver. Then he filled his bucket with the wishing worms. Now he was ready to go to the river.

98

Oliver didn't go to the dock where Tom and Mike might be fishing. He sat under a big tree near the river bank. He put a wishing worm on his hook, and he put his line into the water.

Then Oliver shut his eyes, and he made a wish. Before he opened his eyes, he felt a pull on the line. He waited a minute and then pulled in the line. He had caught a round, fat sunfish!

Soon there were eight sunfish on Oliver's string. "Wishing worms do work," thought Oliver. He didn't feel awful now! But he was getting tired.

There were only two wishing worms left. Oliver gave one worm to a turtle, and he popped the last one into his own mouth.

Oliver shut his eyes and made a wish. Suddenly he heard someone call his name. Then he saw Tom and Mike.

"Where have you been?" asked Tom. "We've been looking all over for you."

"We thought you would come to the dock when you woke up," Mike said.

"And I thought you didn't want me to fish with you," Oliver said.

The boys laughed. At last the confusion was over.

"Look at Oliver's fish!" Tom shouted.

"All I did was wish for them," Oliver laughed. "Now I can ask you and Mike and Mr. Crummel to a big fish dinner!"

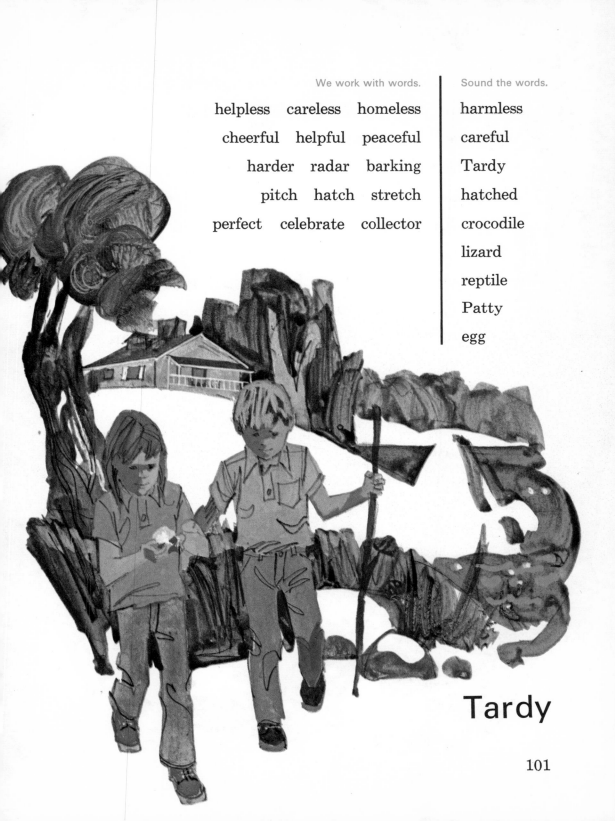

helpless   careless   homeless

cheerful   helpful   peaceful

harder   radar   barking

pitch   hatch   stretch

perfect   celebrate   collector

harmless

careful

Tardy

hatched

crocodile

lizard

reptile

Patty

egg

Tardy

Patty and Jim walked down to the river, carrying some bread to feed the fish. Patty dropped her bread into the water, and she watched the tiny fish snap it up. Then she sat back in the warm sand.

"I like living by the river," said Patty. "But I wish we had a pet."

"Mom says we can keep a pet if we find one that's small and quiet," Jim said.

"But I never find anything that's small and quiet around here," sighed Patty.

"Well, let's play awhile in the sand," said Jim. Just then Jim's hand ran across something round. "There's something in the sand!" he cried.

Jim was very careful as he pushed away the sand. Patty moved closer. "Eggs!" they both said at once.

"What animal would lay eggs out here?" asked Patty.

"I don't know," Jim said. "I've never seen eggs like these. They don't look like duck or hen eggs. They are too round," he added.

"Let's put sand over them again," said Patty. "They just might hatch small, quiet animals." She was careful not to be rough with the eggs.

"I'll put a stick in the sand so we can find this place again," Jim said.

At supper Patty and Jim told their father about the eggs.

"An animal put them in the sand," said Dad. "She wants the sun to keep them warm so they will hatch."

"But what animal could it have been?" Jim asked.

"A reptile," answered Dad.

"You mean those are snake eggs?" Patty asked in a scared voice.

"Well, maybe not," said Dad, laughing. "Snakes are not the only reptiles. The eggs could be crocodile eggs."

"Crocodile eggs!" shouted Patty.

"Dad is joking," said Jim.

Dad laughed. "There are no crocodiles around here," he said. "So those are not crocodile eggs. I'm sure harmless animals will hatch."

"Maybe they are lizard eggs," said Jim. "Lizards are harmless reptiles."

"Let's wait and see," said Dad. "I think you'll have a nice surprise."

Every day after that, Jim and his sister hurried to the river to see if the eggs had hatched.

"I'm afraid they'll be snakes," Patty said. "And I want a harmless little pet."

"I hope they'll be lizards," said Jim.

"I don't think the eggs will ever hatch," sighed Patty.

"Dad says it won't take much longer," said Jim.

That day Patty and Jim went shopping with their mother. By the time they returned, it was too late to go to the river and see about the eggs.

So the next morning Patty and Jim raced to the river. When they reached the sand, they stopped suddenly. Eggshells were all around.

"Look!" cried Patty. "The eggs hatched while we were shopping. I guess we'll never find a pet now!"

Jim pointed to the strange tracks going into the river. "And we'll never know what was in the eggs," he said.

"Wait a minute!" Patty cried. "Here's an egg that hasn't hatched."

They both watched as the egg began to move. "It's cracking," whispered Jim.

"I think I see a little head under the eggshells," Patty said.

Before long a funny little head pushed through a crack in the shell.

"It looks like a snake," cried Patty.

"No, it looks like a lizard," said Jim.

"It can't be a crocodile," said Patty.

They kept watching. Soon a small reptile pushed out of the shell.

"It's a turtle!" they shouted together.

"We'll have a pet after all," said Jim. And he was very careful as he picked up the little turtle.

"He was so late coming out of his shell," said Patty. "Let's name him Tardy."

Then Patty and Jim ran to the house to show off Tardy, their new pet.

Think about This:

Does a turtle make a good pet?
How are a crocodile and a turtle alike? How are they different?

107

The River Is a Piece of Sky

From the top of a bridge

The river below

Is a piece of sky—

Until you throw

A penny in

Or a cockleshell

Or a pebble or two

Or a bicycle bell

Or a cobblestone

Or a fat man's cane—

And then you can see

It's a river again.

The difference you'll see

When you drop your penny:

The river has splashes,

The sky hasn't any.

by John Ciardi

108

sudden   bottom   problem   seldom

large   gently   ginger   gym   barges

lazier   mysteries   happiest   cities

elephant   dolphin   telephone   phone

fullest   butcher   pulls   pushes

square   spare   glare   aware

already   below   awoke   ago

tow

radar

pilot

There Go the Towboats

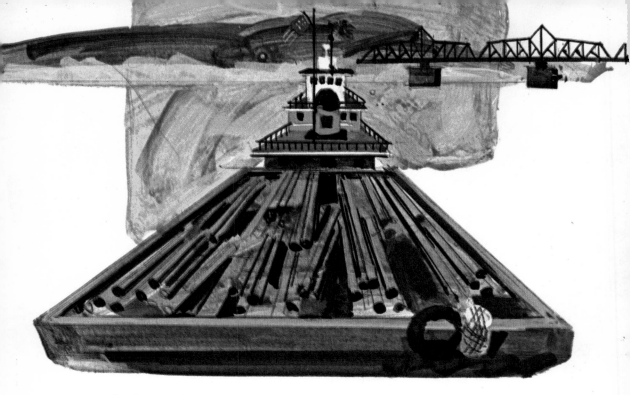

A big river can be a highway for boats. If you travel along a big river, you will become aware of long lines of barges. They are being moved along the river by towboats. The barges carry heavy loads of iron and steel to cities by the river.

Today a towboat doesn't tow or pull the barges. It pushes them. But the towboat got its name long ago when it did tow barges. The way the towboat works has changed, but its name is still the same.

Towboats can push barges better than they can pull them. Barges are tied together with steel ropes and are locked in place in front of the towboat. The towboat pilot seldom has trouble moving the barges.

But a river pilot's job is seldom an easy one. The pilot must know the river. He must be aware of the small boats which sail all around him.

If a small boat gets in front of the big barges, there could be trouble. The towboat can't stop quickly because the barges are heavy. A small boat may be crushed if it is hit by a barge.

A towboat has many things to help the
river pilot. It has radar to help him get
through the fog. Radar will also let him
know if another boat is near at night.

A towboat has a phone that the pilot can
use to give an order to other men on the
boat. It has another special phone that
he can use to call the riverman at the
bridge. Then the riverman will open the
bridge, and the pilot can take his boat on
through.

It is very important for the river pilot
and the riverman to work together.

action   questions   section
wounded   troupe   croup
handful   peaceful   playful
dare   bare   share
baker   loved   closed

direction

group

helpful

spare

waved

catwalk

downstream

handle

cabin

Steve Becomes a Riverman

When Steve was with his uncle, he felt that someday he wanted to be a riverman, too. Steve thought it was fun to sit in the little cabin under the bridge. He liked watching his uncle open the bridge to let the boats go through.

One day as he sat beside his uncle, Steve heard the toot of a whistle downstream.

"It's the *Peter J.* coming up with a heavy load," said Uncle Fred.

Below the bridge, Steve saw the towboat pushing a group of barges.

"They won't get up here for a long time," Uncle Fred said.

"The *Peter J.* is a fierce little boat," said Steve. "Look at its load!"

"Towboats can push heavy loads," said Uncle Fred. "But barges are hard to handle if the stream is swift. When a barge hits a bridge, there's trouble."

Suddenly they heard a whistle from the other direction. Another towboat with some barges was coming down the river.

"That towboat is in a hurry!" said Uncle Fred. Quickly he pushed the button that started the red lights blinking. Then the gate that closed off the bridge came down, and all the cars stopped.

"The barges are coming too fast!" cried Steve.

"The pilot on the towboat can't slow them down!" said Uncle Fred. Quickly he pushed a handle, and the bridge began to open.

Steve and Uncle Fred watched the pilot work to get the group of barges through the bridge opening. The pilot waved and gave a toot on his whistle. Steve waved back.

Then Uncle Fred moved another handle, and the bridge came together. The gate went up, and the red lights stopped blinking. Cars began to move across the bridge.

"That was a close call!" Steve cried. "You must feel good to be so helpful!"

"Yes, I like being helpful," said Uncle Fred. "But the *Peter J.* must hurry if I'm going to open the bridge for it."

They watched the little towboat trying to push the heavy barges up the stream.

"Poor *Peter J.*," said Steve. "The water is pushing the barges out of line."

But Uncle Fred opened the bridge, and the *Peter J.* came through. Then he closed the bridge after the boat had passed.

"It's time for me to stop work," said Uncle Fred. "Come along. I have to sign out. Mr. King will take over soon."

Steve followed his uncle up the ladder to the catwalk. Then Steve looked down at the river.

"Uncle Fred!" he shouted. "Look at the *Peter J.*" The swift stream had caught the barges and turned them around. Now they were racing downstream to the bridge. The pilot blew his whistle. What confusion! The bridge had to be opened—and fast!

Uncle Fred turned quickly to go back to the cabin. But he bumped against the fence along the catwalk. "Oh, my leg!" moaned Uncle Fred. "I'll never make it. Run, Steve! Open the bridge. Hurry!"

Steve ran. He climbed down the ladder
and rushed into the cabin. He pushed the
button to start the red lights on the bridge.
The gate came down in place.

"Now the big handle is next," thought
Steve. He moved it, and the bridge began
to swing out. Steve looked up the river at
the *Peter J.*

The pilot kept the barges away from the
side of the bridge—with room to spare. At
last the towboat got through the opening!

Steve's hand shook as he reached for the handle to close the bridge again.   Just then Mr. King came into the cabin.

"Where is Fred?" he shouted.

Steve told about all the confusion.

"I thought the barges were sure to hit the bridge," sighed Mr. King. "But you got here with time to spare!"

"Why did the barges turn back in this direction?" asked Steve.

"It was the rough water," said Mr. King. "That pilot almost lost his load!"

"What will the pilot of the *Peter J.* do now?" asked Steve.

"I hope he'll wait until the river is quiet again," said Mr. King. "It was lucky for him that we had a spare riverman on the bridge today!"

Steve smiled. Mr. King had called him a riverman. Now Steve felt sure that someday he would be a riverman.

Think about This:

What did Steve learn from Uncle Fred? How did it help him?

If Steve had not opened the bridge, how would this story have ended?

proves   movers   canoe

golden   fallen   broken

nicely   hopeful   strangely

dialed   triangle   rodeo

month   dozen   love

wrinkle   bingo   uncles

canoes

hidden

peaceful

Indian

loved

angry

trotline

cove

Sight word.

spirit

Mississippi Pete

Pete's Cove

Pete felt sure that the best place to live was along the Mississippi River.

The big lazy river rolled slowly past the front door of his house. Back of his house were hills with Indian trails to follow and rocks to climb.

Pete liked to sit and watch the river. Sometimes he saw big white boats filled with people laughing and singing. Some days there were boats that pushed great barges carrying heavy loads of iron.

Best of all Pete liked the old boat that his dad had helped him repair. They kept the boat hidden in Pete's Cove on a creek.

One day when Pete and Dad were near the cove, Pete asked, "Did the Indians tie up their canoes here in the old days?"

"I wouldn't be surprised!" answered Dad. "They used to make canoes from trees like these."

"Then they could go down the creek and out to the river," said Pete.

"And people used to say," his dad added, "that the spirit of the Indians watched over all who loved the river."

"I wish I knew more about that spirit," said Pete. He closed his eyes and tried to see the canoes coming up the creek to Pete's Cove.

But today Pete must be on his way to look over his trotlines. He hurried along the trails to the creek. No air was moving, and all was peaceful.

Pete looked at the sky. "Mom said a storm was coming," he thought as he walked along. "So I won't go far."

Pete's boat was right where he had left it. He found his oars hidden in the tall grass. Then he pushed his boat out into the water and jumped in. Oh, how Pete loved everything about the river!

Then he rowed down the creek and pulled each trotline out of the water. But there were no fish on the trotlines.

Pete put down his oars and let his boat float along. Then he stretched out on the floor of the boat, and he looked up at the peaceful sky. Pete felt sleepy, and soon his eyes closed.

Before long the sky became dark, and the wind began to blow. The river was no longer peaceful. It seemed angry now.

We work with words.

Sound the words.

extra	explode	excited	explain
fallen	frighten	wooden	frightened
cherry	tomorrow	barrel	arrow
			canoe

The Storm

Suddenly Pete sat up in the old boat and looked around. Everything was different. This wasn't the creek. His boat was out on the river! There were big waves all around. Then he began to hear thunder. Pete was frightened!

125

Pete tried to row back to land, but the waves were too strong for him. Now he was more frightened!

"I can't jump out and swim," thought Pete. "This water is too rough. It's so rough I can't even row the boat!"

He heard more thunder. But there was no rain. The clouds were low. It was hard to see. He looked back at Pete's Cove, and all he could see was gray fog over the land and water.

Then he looked again. "Is that a boat coming out of the cove?" he thought. "It looks like a canoe!"

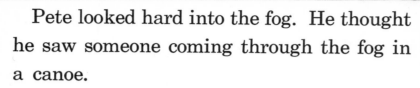

Pete looked hard into the fog. He thought he saw someone coming through the fog in a canoe.

"Help! I need help!" called Pete.

But the wind carried the sound of his voice away. He looked into the fog, and he saw the man in the canoe pick up something. "He must be an Indian," Pete thought.

In an instant an arrow hit Pete's boat. He could see a rope tied to the arrow. But there wasn't a sound. The Indian moved his oars through the water as he pulled both boats up into the creek.

"It is an Indian!" thought Pete. "It has to be an Indian!"

Suddenly there were big angry flashes of lightning across the sky. Then the wind began to blow in a different direction. It blew Pete's boat near the cove. Pete looked for the Indian. But he was gone!

Then Pete looked at the front of his boat. "The arrow and the rope are gone!" he cried.

Pete grabbed his oars and rowed up the creek into Pete's Cove. He tied his boat to some rocks and started home. He met his dad along the trail.

"Hurry, Pete!" called Dad. "The storm is getting bad. Run as fast as you can!" They ran through the rain to their house.

When they were inside, Pete did his best to explain what happened. "I couldn't see very well, but I'm sure it was an Indian," he told them.

"Why do you say that?" asked Mother.

"His canoe was made from wood like our trees," said Pete. "And no one else could have rowed against that wind."

"Now, now," said Mother. "You know there have been no Indians around here for a long time. It was just the wind pushing you. That will explain how you got back to the cove. I wish Dad wouldn't tell you those Indian tales!"

When Mother returned to the kitchen, Pete looked at his dad. A smile spread across Dad's face.

Pete didn't say very much while they ate supper. He was making plans. In the morning he would start looking for the Indian who pulled in his boat!

We work with words.

exact example exactly

kindness darkness sadness

exchange expect excited

paper visitor beggar

permission mansion

Sight word.

Dr.

Sound the words.

examine

illness

explained

collar

television

Tony

rabies

flu

Sally

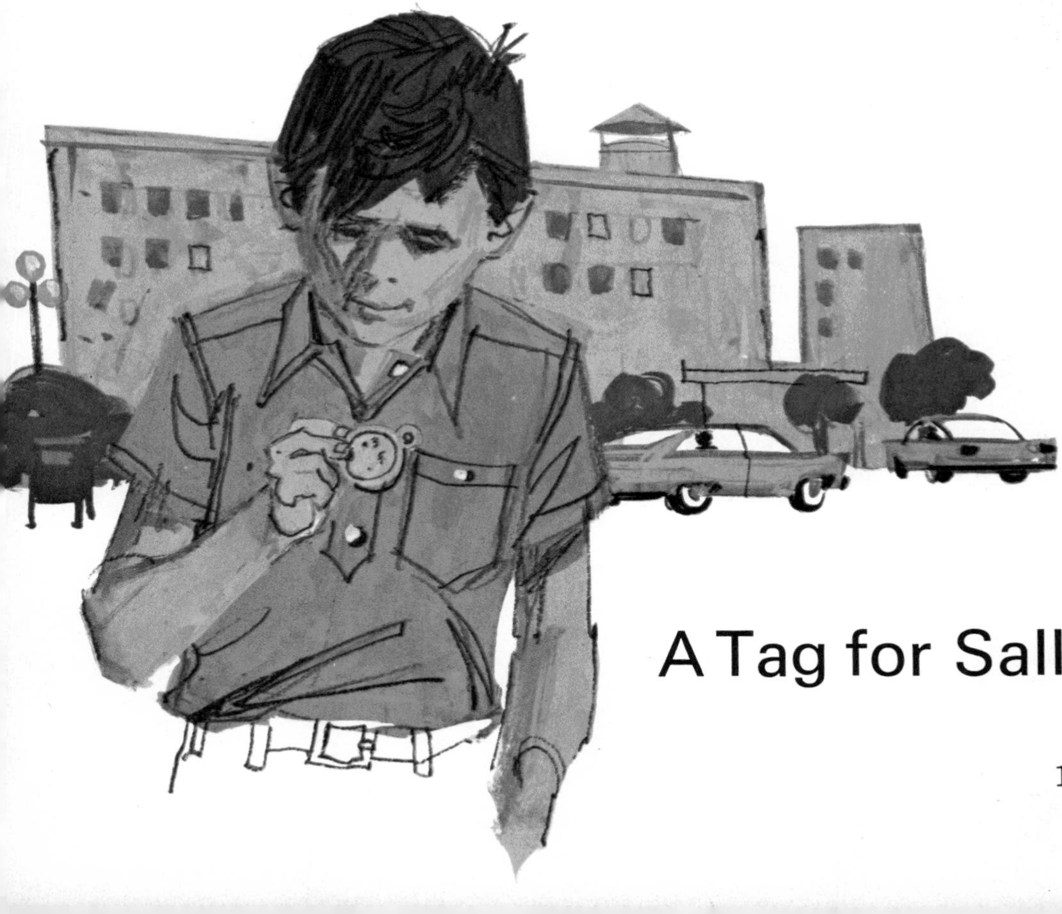

A Tag for Sally

Tony brought the newspaper into the kitchen. "Mother, does this mean I have to take Sally?" he asked.

"Take Sally where?" his mother asked.

Tony read from the newspaper, "Bring your dog to the fire station for rabies shot and dog tag next Saturday."

"Yes, you'll have to take Sally," said Tony's mother. "She needs a new dog tag and a rabies shot, too."

"Will the shot hurt Sally?" Tony asked.

"The rabies shot doesn't hurt as much as the illness," answered his mother. "Your flu shot didn't hurt you, did it?"

Tony thought it over. When he had his flu shot, it didn't really hurt. But he had been scared. Would Sally be scared?

The next day Tony went to see Ted, who lived next door. Ted had a dog, too.

"I'm not going to take my dog for a shot," said Ted. "Dogs seldom get rabies. So why hurt the poor little dogs?"

"Do you think it really hurts them?" Tony asked.

"You just go to the fire station, and you will hear a group of dogs barking!" said Ted. "Don't tell me the shot doesn't hurt!"

Tony walked home slowly. It was harder to hurt Sally than to be hurt himself.

That night Tony told his dad and mother what Ted had said.

"I don't believe Ted is right," said Dad. "Sally needs a rabies shot. You don't want to be the cause of Sally's illness."

"And Dr. Flood can examine Sally for any other illness she might have," explained Mother.

When Saturday came, Tony found many things to do. "I can't take Sally," he told his dad. "I have too much to do."

"Now, Tony," Dad said. "We can't keep a dog that might get rabies. If you want to keep Sally, you must take her to the fire station for her shot."

Tony stood still for a while trying to think of a way out. But he couldn't. So at last he snapped the leash on Sally's collar and started down the street.

As Tony got near the fire station, he could hear dogs barking. Sally looked up at him. Her eyes seemed to say, "What is this all about?"

He could feel Sally shaking. How could he take her inside that place?

Just then Tony saw something shiny on the sidewalk. He picked it up to examine it. It was a dog tag!

"What luck!" said Tony. "I'll put it on Sally, and everyone will think she has had her rabies shot."

135

Tony didn't go home right away. He walked Sally around the block. When he got home, he hooked the tag onto Sally's collar. Then he went into the living room, where he found his mother watching television.

"See Sally's new tag?" Tony said.

Mother turned off the television. "Fine," she said. "Now give me the paper."

"What paper?" asked Tony.

"The paper that shows Sally has had a rabies shot," said Mother. "Didn't you get one?"

Tony could feel his face turning red, and his hand was shaking. "No, I didn't get a paper," he said.

"We know that Sally has had her rabies shot," Mother explained. "But if she got sick, we would need to show the paper to the doctor. Then he would know that rabies couldn't be the cause of her illness."

Tony sat down. Sally lay by his feet. What if Sally should get rabies?

Suddenly Tony stood up. "We're going
back to the fire station," he said. "Come
on, Sally."

When Tony and Sally came to the station,
they stood in line behind other children
with their dogs. Tony watched each dog get
its shot. Not one barked.

"Oh, Sally," he whispered. "I hope you
will be as good as they are!"

Now it was Sally's turn. Dr. Flood smiled
at Tony as he put Sally on the table. In
an instant it was all over. Sally didn't
make a sound!

Tony hooked the leash on Sally's collar. Then he took the tag he had found to a lady at the front desk. "I found this dog tag on the sidewalk," he explained.

The lady held the dog tag up close to examine the writing. "Thank you, Tony," she said. "Someone will be looking for this tag. Here is Sally's new tag and a paper showing that she has had a rabies shot."

Sally was pulling on her leash. So they started for home. "See, that's all there is to it, Sally," said Tony. "No need to worry now. You won't get rabies, and you have your own tag!"

We work with words.

sure treasure measure

narrator sailor collector

Sight words.

toothache Whoosh

Sound the words.

pleasure

operator

rickety

elevator

dentist

rocket

louder

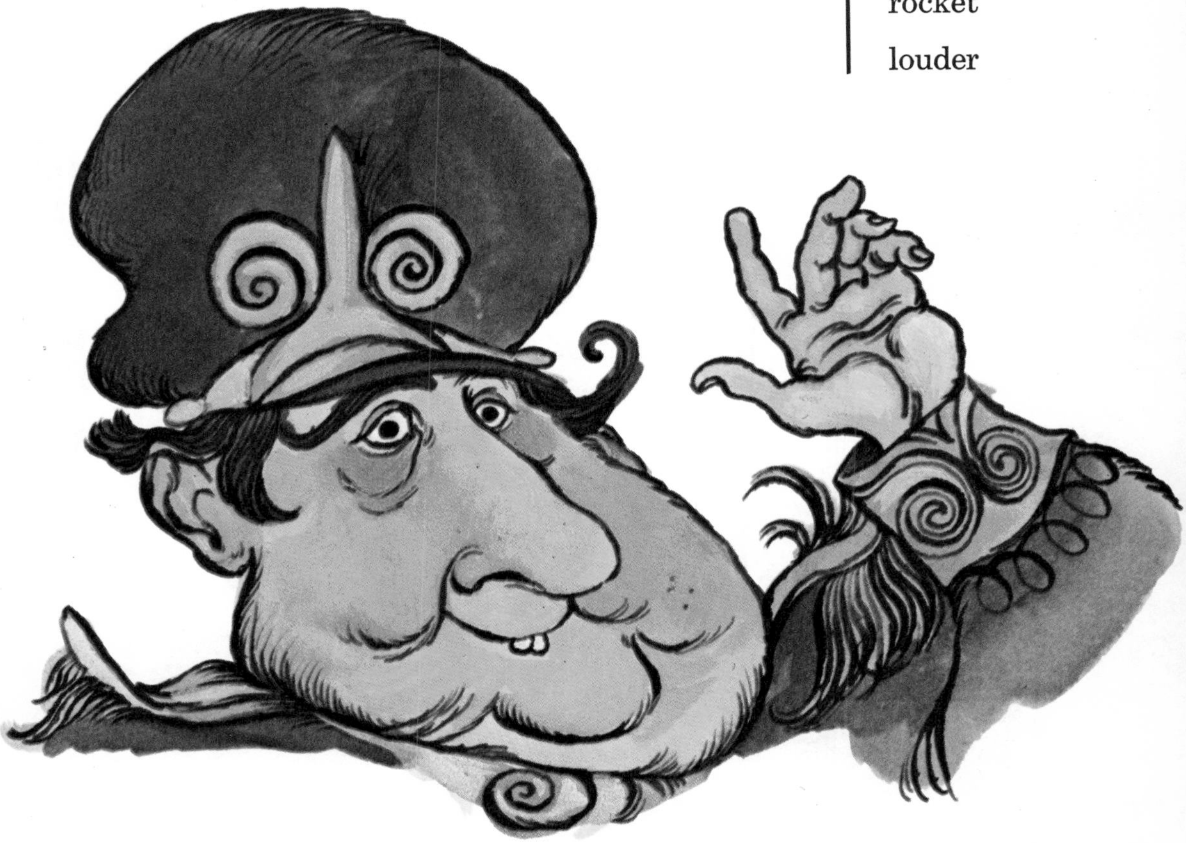

Oliver, the Elevator Operator

Once upon a time, in a tall building, there was a rickety old elevator. Oliver was the elevator operator. He wore a green coat with big, shiny buttons.

"Good morning!" said Oliver to people who rode his elevator. "Going up!"

Everyone liked Oliver. But his rickety old elevator didn't always work just the way it should. Sometimes when Oliver pushed the handle down, the elevator went up. And sometimes when he pushed the handle up, the elevator went down. There were even times when it didn't go at all.

But Oliver was a good elevator operator. He could always fix the old elevator. Then once again it would take everyone to the right floor. So Oliver kept people happy.

One day a man who worked on the top floor had a bad toothache. He wanted to get to a dentist right away. So he hurried down the hall, and he pushed the button to ring for the elevator.

"I need to go down at once!" he cried.

"There's a call from the top floor," said Oliver. He pushed the handle up. But that rickety old elevator went down.

"I must get to a dentist at once!" the man with the toothache shouted. Again he pushed the button to ring for the elevator.

"Just a minute! I'm coming!" Oliver said. He pushed the handle up. Nothing happened! He pushed the handle down. Still nothing happened.

"Oh! My toothache! Oh!" cried the man on the top floor. He pushed the button harder and harder and harder. So the bell sounded louder and louder and louder.

All this noise upset Oliver. He pushed the handle hard—harder than he had ever pushed it before.

"Whoosh!" went the elevator.

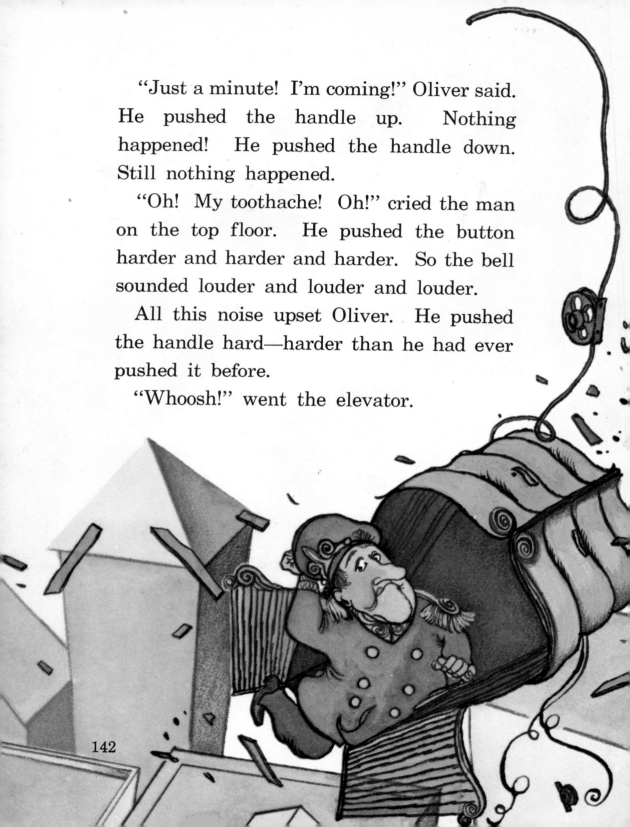

142

The elevator went up like a rocket! Up, up, up it went, past the first floor, past the second floor, up, up, up to the very top floor, and then—still up! Whoosh! Oliver and the old elevator went right out through the roof of the building. And the next minute they were sailing away over the city!

"Oh, dear me!" cried Oliver. "Where am I going?" He pushed the handle this way and that. But he couldn't keep from sailing straight into some birds. One of the birds came flying through the bars of the elevator and sat on Oliver's head.

"This will never do!" cried Oliver. Then he pushed the bird out through the bars. When he looked up, he saw he was about to fly straight into a very tall building. A pretty girl was standing at one of the high windows.

"What are you doing?" she shouted. "Who are you?"

"I'm Eliver! No, not Eliver. Olivator! I'm Olivator the operator!" Oliver shouted back in confusion. "Watch out!"

But Oliver didn't hit the building. At the last minute he pushed the handle, and the elevator turned sideways.

"Why, this is a pleasure!" Oliver cried in surprise. "I can guide the elevator like an airplane!"

With great care, Oliver started back to his own building. He really did think it was a pleasure to fly the elevator. Soon he was over the hole in the roof. He pushed the handle down.

"No airplane pilot ever made a better landing!" Oliver said as he stopped on the top floor. And there stood the poor man with the toothache.

"Down, sir?" asked Oliver.

"Yes, I do want to go down!" shouted the man. "Where have you been? And what was all that noise? For a minute I thought the roof blew off!"

Oliver wished he could tell the man about the pleasure of elevator flying. But there wasn't time to tell the story now. He had to get the man to a dentist.

"Going down, sir!" said Oliver.

Think about This:

Why didn't Oliver tell the man with the toothache what had happened?
In what ways did the elevator seem like a rocket?

We work with words.

extra   example   excite

insure   surely   measured

actor   governor   conductor

broken   frozen   beaten

flashed   fiercely   peaceful

potato   aroma   happens   pajamas

Sight words.

Hawaii   Island   palm

Sound the words.

excited

treasure

collector

fallen

strangely

problem

cover

Janet

code

beginning

math

Bookstore Mystery

After lunch Janet called her friend, Alice. "I'm going to help Aunt Dee at the bookstore this afternoon," she said. "Do you want to go with me?"

"Yes!" answered Alice in an excited voice. "It's fun to look through all of her old books. And I like the things she has that were made in Hawaii, too."

Later at the bookstore, the two girls were going through some old books.

"Most of these books are about Hawaii," Janet said as she stacked some books on the top shelf.

"Here are some old storybooks and some schoolbooks," said Alice. "Someone has drawn pictures of ships on this math book."

"Here's the book *Treasure Island* that must have been used by the same boy," said Janet. "There are pictures of ships inside the cover."

Janet held up the book, and a small paper fell out. "Look, this paper has numbers all over it," she said. "It looks as if it should be in a math book. But I never saw a problem like that."

"Let's see," said Alice as she picked up the small paper. "At the beginning it has 4–5–1–18 x 2–15–2. And those numbers are followed by more numbers."

Alice and Janet both looked at the paper again. "I know!" Janet cried in an excited voice. "It's a message in code!"

Just then some people came into the store. So the girls did not have time to think about the paper again.

The next day an older boy brought some books into the shop. "I would like to sell some old books," the boy told Aunt Dee. "I'm going away to school, and these extra books are in the way now."

"A book collector is always glad to get your extra books," said Aunt Dee. "Put these up on the shelf, Janet."

One book Janet picked up had a ship on the back cover. The ship looked strangely like the one drawn on the math book and the storybook.

The next morning an excited Janet took the paper with the numbers on it over to Alice's house. She told her about the older boy bringing in a book with a ship drawn on it.

"I wonder if he's the boy who made the ships on those other books," said Alice.

"Let's see if we can work out the code," said Janet. "That might tell us something."

Just as Janet spread out the paper, Alice's brother Stan walked into the room. They told him about the mystery of the books.

"We have a code problem," said Janet.

"Try this," Stan said. "Let the number 1 stand for *a*, the number 2 for *b*, and so on. See what happens."

The note looked like this—

4-5-1-18 X 2-15-2
9 X 1-13 X 19-15-18-18-25 X 9 X
23-1-19 X 13-5-1-14 X 25-15-21-18 X
19-20-1-18 X 1-14-4 X 16-1-12-13-19 X
1-18-5 X 9-14 X 20-8-5 X 3-15-22-5-18 X
7-5-20 X 23-5-12-12 X 19-15-15-14 X
10-15-5

"Stan's idea must be **right**," shouted Alice. "See, the first four numbers are 4–5–1–18. That would be d–e–a–r, like the beginning of a note."

"Yes, and the words are kept apart by an *x*," explained Stan.

It took some time, but they came up with the answer to the code. Stan wrote down the words as the girls worked out the code. Then he read the note to them.

"Dear Bob, I am sorry I was mean. Your star and palms are in the cover. Get well soon. Joe."

"I don't understand," said Janet. "What can *star* and *palms* mean? And what cover? It's still a mystery!"

"Could it mean the cover of the book *Treasure Island?*" asked Alice.

That night Janet asked Aunt Dee for the *Treasure Island* book. Then Janet looked at the cover. She didn't see a star or palms. But when she put the book down, she saw that a small paper had fallen out of it. When Janet picked up the paper, she found that it was a blue stamp.

"Oh, it has a star and palm trees on it!" cried Janet. "And it looks very old!"

Just then the door opened, and in walked the same boy, carrying more books. Janet still had the stamp in her hand. "Did you ever have the book *Treasure Island?*" she asked.

The boy looked at Janet strangely. "No, I didn't, but I think my brother did. Why?"

"This stamp has fallen out of the book," said Janet. "It must be your stamp."

Then Janet went to the table to get the book and the note. The boy smiled. "I used to be a stamp collector. One day my brother and I had a fight. After the fight he was angry, so he hid this stamp. I was sick at the time and forgot about his note."

"Well, here's your stamp," said Janet.

"Oh no, you take it," said the boy. "I'm not a collector now. It's an old stamp that was used in Hawaii long ago!"

"I'll give it to Alice's brother," said Janet. "He's a stamp collector. And he helped us work out the code. Thanks for helping us work out the mystery!"

We work with words.

furnace   garbage   village

through   cousin   fought

dinnertime   footprints   leftover

wrestling   wiggled   stranger

Sight word.

busy

Sound the words.

package

ought

sunshine

stared

appear

crazy

army

Trudy

Stevens

watered

helmet

Flower Street

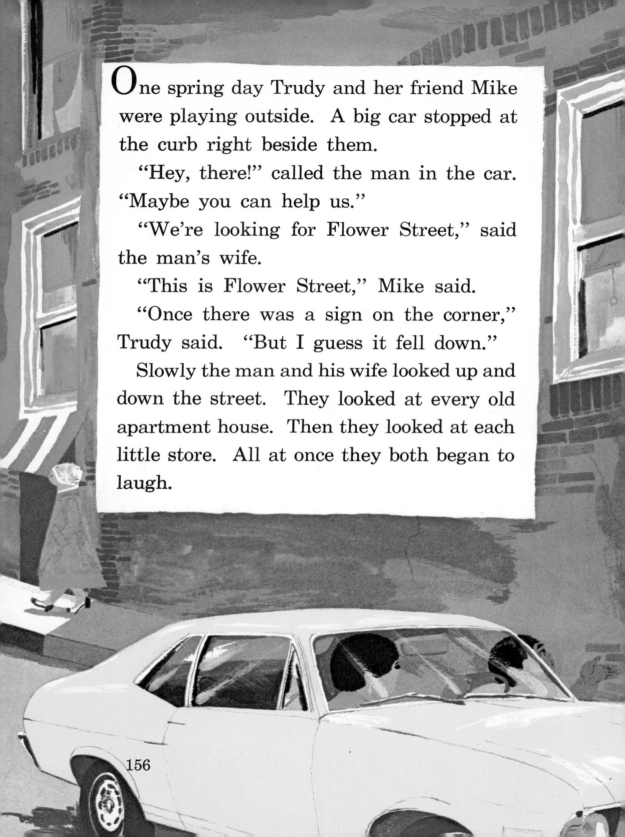

One spring day Trudy and her friend Mike were playing outside. A big car stopped at the curb right beside them.

"Hey, there!" called the man in the car. "Maybe you can help us."

"We're looking for Flower Street," said the man's wife.

"This is Flower Street," Mike said.

"Once there was a sign on the corner," Trudy said. "But I guess it fell down."

Slowly the man and his wife looked up and down the street. They looked at every old apartment house. Then they looked at each little store. All at once they both began to laugh.

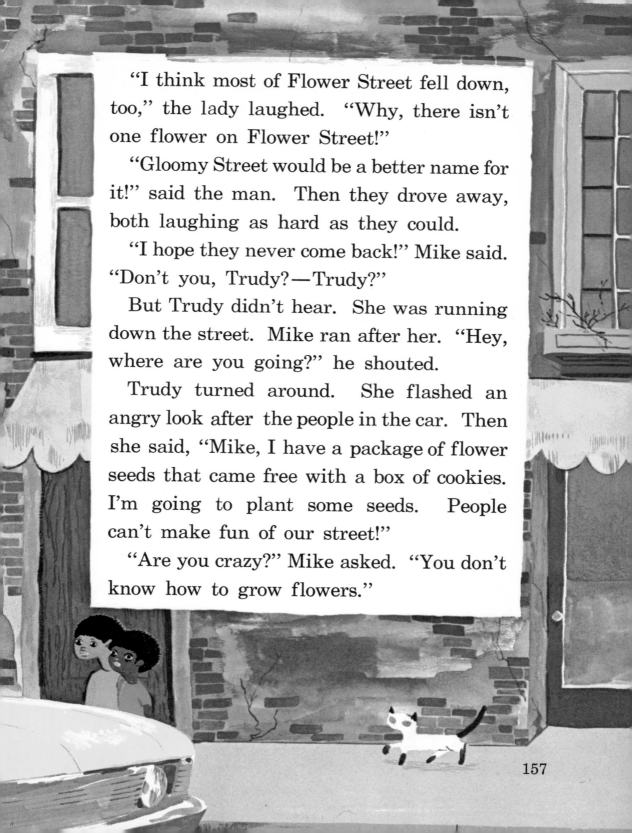

"I think most of Flower Street fell down, too," the lady laughed. "Why, there isn't one flower on Flower Street!"

"Gloomy Street would be a better name for it!" said the man. Then they drove away, both laughing as hard as they could.

"I hope they never come back!" Mike said. "Don't you, Trudy?—Trudy?"

But Trudy didn't hear. She was running down the street. Mike ran after her. "Hey, where are you going?" he shouted.

Trudy turned around. She flashed an angry look after the people in the car. Then she said, "Mike, I have a package of flower seeds that came free with a box of cookies. I'm going to plant some seeds. People can't make fun of our street!"

"Are you crazy?" Mike asked. "You don't know how to grow flowers."

"Well, I can learn," Trudy said. "And there ought to be flowers on Flower Street. Don't you think so, Mike?"

"Trudy, the street got its name a long time ago," Mike said. "There were lots and lots of flowers then. But now people are too busy to grow flowers."

"I'm not too busy!" Trudy said. "Are you going to help me or not?"

"Oh, all right," Mike said. "But growing flowers is a crazy idea."

Mike went with Trudy to get the package of seeds. Then he helped her find things to use for flowerpots. She planted seeds in bowls, cups, and jars. She even planted seeds in an old army helmet.

"Why didn't you plant the seeds in one of the window boxes?" Mike asked.

"Because I have a plan," said Trudy. Then she whispered her plan to Mike.

"You and your crazy ideas!" laughed Mike. But he helped her carry the funny flower pots to the roof of the apartment house.

No one was more surprised than Mike when the seeds did come up! Soon there were green stems in all the cups, bowls, and jars. And the biggest stems of all were in the old army helmet.

"Is it time yet?" Mike asked Trudy.

"No, not yet," she said.

After a few days of warm sunshine, buds began to appear on the stems. Trudy watered the plants every day. Mike dug up the dirt around them. He kept turning the plants so they would get enough sunshine.

At last the buds opened. Yellow flowers began to appear. "Trudy, is it time yet?" Mike asked.

"No, not yet," said Trudy.

Every day there were more and more
yellow flowers. Trudy watered them and
took care of them until the roof top looked
like a country garden. "Trudy, it really
ought to be time now," Mike said.

"Yes, Mike," said Trudy. "Now it's time."

"At last!" Mike said. Then he took the
army helmet of flowers to Mr. Stevens at
the bookstore.

"Mr. Stevens, Trudy wants to give you
these flowers," Mike said. "She hopes you
will put them in the window."

Then Mike took flowers to all the stores
along Flower Street. Trudy took flowers to
every apartment with a window box. How
very surprised people were by the flowers!

All at once Flower Street didn't look the same. Mike and Trudy just couldn't believe how different it looked. There were yellow flowers in almost every window. Everyone came outside to look at the flowers. People in cars pointed and stared. A newspaper man came to take pictures of the bookstore.

"Wait!" Mr. Stevens told him. "Mike and Trudy are the ones who ought to have their pictures taken."

The next day there were pictures of Trudy and Mike in the newspaper! There were two pictures of Flower Street as well. Under the pictures, were the words—

TRUDY AND MIKE
BRING FLOWERS BACK
TO FLOWER STREET

"Trudy, your idea wasn't so crazy after all!" Mike laughed. "I hope those people who made fun of us see the newspaper."

"So do I," said Trudy. "And people are really taking care of the flowers, Mike. I've heard some people say they will plant other flowers, too."

"Yes, flowers have come back to Flower Street," Mike said. "I think they have come back to stay!"

Think about This:

What might Trudy have done if Mike hadn't helped her?

Find out how a street in your city got its name.

163

The Seed

How does it know,
this little seed,
if it is to grow
to a flower or weed,
if it is to be
a vine or shoot,
or grow to a tree
with a long deep root?
A seed is so small.
Where do you suppose
it stores up all
of the things it knows?

by Aileen Fisher

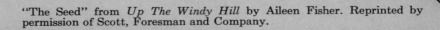

"The Seed" from *Up The Windy Hill* by Aileen Fisher. Reprinted by permission of Scott, Foresman and Company.

We work with words.

safety   property   forty

argument   excitement   payment

butcher   bullet   pulley

Sound the words.

sixty

apartments

July

potato

inches

begin

Irish

City Garden

165

Many city people like to grow plants. But in the crowded city, it's hard to find a place for a garden. People living in city apartments don't have a yard where they can plant seeds. Still they do find ways to grow plants both inside and outside their apartments.

Some city people grow flowers and other plants in window boxes. On a hot July day, it's nice to see a window box crowded with pretty flowers. And some window boxes can be taken inside when winter comes. There pretty flowers will grow all winter long, not just in July.

It's easy to grow plants in a flowerpot. People everywhere from six to sixty have fun watching their plants grow.

Some indoor plants are grown from seeds. But plants can also be grown from roots or stems. Beets are roots, and pretty green plants can be grown from them. An Irish potato is a stem, and a plant can be grown from its eyes.

An Irish potato plant is easy to grow. Would you like to grow one yourself? Here are the things you will need.

part of a potato with one or two eyes

flowerpot filled with dirt

dish to put under flowerpot

Push the potato part about four inches down into the dirt. Then cover it well with dirt. Give it enough water to make the dirt very wet.

Soon a plant will begin to grow from the potato eyes. It will need plenty of water. You may need to water it four or five times a week. Don't let the dirt become dry.

There are other plants you can grow in the city, too. About all you will need is a flowerpot and a few inches of dirt. Your library should have some books about these plants.

Why not begin an indoor garden today? Don't wait until you're sixty.

contain   captain   mountain

grateful   mouthful   thankful

baggage   packages   cottage

ladies   funniest   worried

actor   inventor   visitor

spaghetti   chili   Morelli

curtain

wonderful

cabbage

families

visitors

secret

Moy

aroma

Ryan

Porto

What's Cooking?

Twelve families lived in the Lakewood Apartments. The old three-story building seemed like a tree as the boys and girls visited back and forth. They rushed up and down the stairs, chattering like little squirrels.

But the mothers and fathers didn't visit with each other. They knew about each other only by the aroma in the hall.

When people on the first floor sniffed spaghetti and meat balls, they were aware that a Mrs. Morelli was cooking dinner. Mmmm!

The aroma of cabbage roll from the second floor told everyone that a Mrs. Kelly was cooking. Mmmm!

Down the hall a Mrs. Porto was cooking some chili. Mmmm!

Upstairs a Mrs. Moy was fixing fish to go with rice for her dinner. Mmmm!

Friendly Mrs. Ryan lived on the first floor. She knew all the children. And she wanted to know all the mothers and fathers. So one day Mrs. Ryan and all the children planned a secret!

That night as people passed Mrs. Ryan's door, they stopped suddenly.

"Mmmm," Mr. Kelly said. "What smells so good on the first floor?"

"Mmmm," said Mr. Morelli. "What can Mrs. Ryan be cooking?"

All the men stood out in the hall in a group. Soon the wives were standing in the hall in another group.

The men seemed happy as they sniffed. But the wives seemed worried. They couldn't guess what Mrs. Ryan was cooking. And the children kept very quiet about the secret they had planned with Mrs. Ryan!

"Let's ask Mrs. Ryan what she's cooking," said Mrs. Porto.

"Yes, let's knock on her door!" said Mrs. Morelli. Then the chattering stopped.

Mrs. Ryan came to the door. When she opened it, that wonderful aroma floated into the hall. The men said, "Mmmm!"

"Come in, friends, and sit down," said Mrs. Ryan to the wives.

So the wives came inside and sat down. Mrs. Ryan had never had so many visitors before.

Mrs. Ryan's visitors didn't say anything for a long time. Then they talked about the weather for a while. At last Mrs. Moy popped up and said, "Please, Mrs. Ryan, we feel worried about what you're cooking!"

"Oh, that!" answered Mrs. Ryan. "It's a special dish I'm cooking for dinner tonight. I'm having friends for dinner."

"How nice," said Mrs. Morelli. "But what is the dish?"

"Oh, that!" said Mrs. Ryan. "I'm sorry, but it's a secret."

The wives were sorry Mrs. Ryan couldn't tell the secret, but they understood. So they all went home to their families.

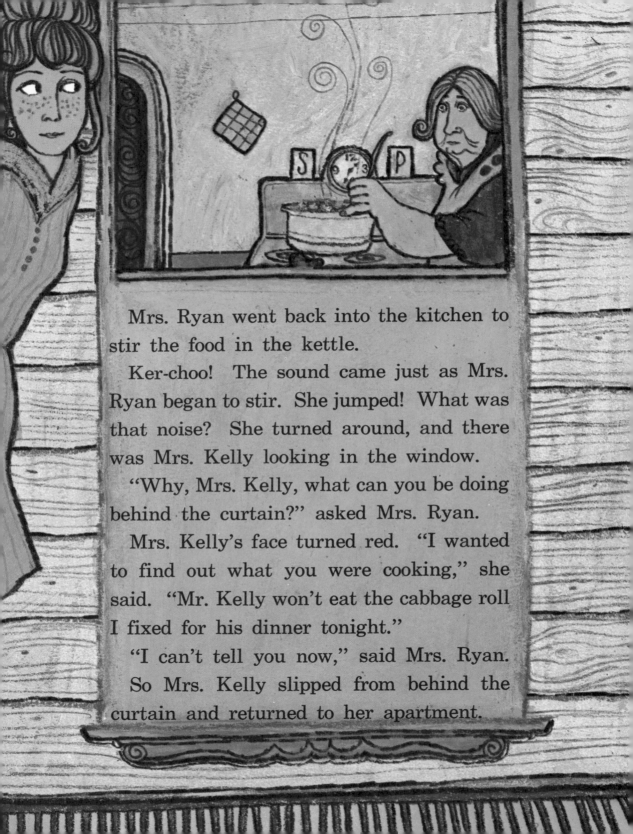

Mrs. Ryan went back into the kitchen to stir the food in the kettle.

Ker-choo! The sound came just as Mrs. Ryan began to stir. She jumped! What was that noise? She turned around, and there was Mrs. Kelly looking in the window.

"Why, Mrs. Kelly, what can you be doing behind the curtain?" asked Mrs. Ryan.

Mrs. Kelly's face turned red. "I wanted to find out what you were cooking," she said. "Mr. Kelly won't eat the cabbage roll I fixed for his dinner tonight."

"I can't tell you now," said Mrs. Ryan.

So Mrs. Kelly slipped from behind the curtain and returned to her apartment.

Soon it was dinnertime. The mothers all called their children to come in. The boys and girls rushed through the hall. They sniffed as they went. "Mmmm!" they sighed. They winked at each other as they passed in the hall. Now they would get to tell part of the secret!

"Mrs. Ryan would like all of our family to come to her apartment for dinner," said Tony Morelli. "She's cooking that new dish for us!" And the other children told this part of the secret to their families.

In a few minutes, everyone was standing in the hall outside Mrs. Ryan's apartment. Very slowly her door opened.

"All of you come in," said Mrs. Ryan. "I see the children told you part of our secret!"

Then Mrs. Ryan gave each friend a plate of food. "This is our secret dish!" she said. "It was made a secret way!"

The boys and girls nodded their heads and winked at one another.

"Tell us how you made your secret dish," said Mrs. Kelly.

"Yes," said Mrs. Porto. "What do we need to make this wonderful dish?"

"First you will need many friends," said Mrs. Ryan. "The children helped me find things for our secret dish."

"You need spaghetti from Mrs. Morelli," said Tony Morelli.

"And cabbage from Mrs. Kelly," said Tim.

"Then chili meat from Mrs. Porto," said Maria.

"With rice from Mrs. Moy," said Ling.

"And a few other things," said Mrs. Ryan. "Each of your children brought one leftover from his house. That is my secret!"

176

"We didn't know that leftover food was so good," said Mrs. Morelli.

"Now we can make the secret dish!" cried Mrs. Kelly.

Then there was a soft knock at the door. Slowly the door opened. It was Mr. Ryan. "Mmmm," he said. "Is this the right apartment?" Everyone laughed as Mrs. Ryan gave him a plate of food.

After that, Mrs. Ryan had a visit with all the mothers and fathers. Almost any day now you can walk past the Lakewood and smell Mrs. Ryan's secret dish cooking in one of the apartments.

SNAKES
ALIVE

We work with words.

jingling   examined   dancer

beanstalk   saleslady   anyway

Sound the words.

poked

carpool

Betsy

Ronnie

Mark

either

The Snake in the Carpool

Hole in a Basket

One day, while walking through some tall grass, Betsy saw a snake. It was a small gray snake with a yellow neck. Betsy liked most wild things, but she had not had a snake before because 1. Her mother didn't like snakes. 2. Her father didn't care for them, either. 3. Her little brother would either try to bite it or hide it if she took it into the house. 4. She had found a snake once before, and her mother had said, "NO SNAKES IN THE HOUSE!"

But her mother had not said, "NO SNAKES OUT OF THE HOUSE." So Betsy caught the snake. Then she quickly went inside and got a small basket and put some grass in it. She put the snake in the basket, closed the top, and left it outside.

The next morning, Betsy got dressed quickly. She had to be ready for the carpool.

This is not a pool that you swim in. No. When Betsy went to school each morning, she went in a car with three other children, Mark, Jill, and Ronnie. And each day one of their mothers would drive them to school. This is called a carpool.

All the children took little things with them to school. It was nice to have something to show the others. So Betsy thought, "I'll take the snake."

When Mark's mother came to pick her up, Betsy got the basket with the snake. She peeked in. Yes, the snake was still there. Betsy climbed in the back seat with Mark, Jill, and Ronnie. She put the basket on the floor beside some boxes.

"What's in the basket, Betsy?" asked Mark.

"It's a secret," said Betsy. "I'll show you in school." Now Betsy began to wonder if her teacher would say, "NO SNAKES!" But she would have to take a chance now.

"Is it something to eat?" asked Ronnie.

"Oh, no," answered Betsy.

The car was bumping along because there were holes in the road. The boxes on the floor were bumping around, and so was the snake basket.

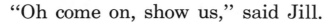

"Oh come on, show us," said Jill.

"You won't be afraid?" asked Betsy.

"Afraid?" said Ronnie. "What is it?"

"All right," said Betsy. "I'll show you."
She put the basket on her lap and opened
the top a crack. "It's under the grass,"
she whispered.

Then she opened the top wide and felt in
the grass with her hand. "It's gone!" Betsy
cried.

"What was it?" asked Mark.

"A snake," Betsy whispered.

"A snake!" said Mark.

"Will it bite?" asked Jill.

"Oh, my poor little snake!" said Betsy.

"Look," whispered Ronnie. "Here's how he got out." He poked his hand in the basket. "There's a hole in the basket."

"We've got to find him," whispered Mark.

They stuck their hands down behind the car seat, and Mark got down to look on the floor.

"It's not any place!" he whispered.

"It has to be," said Betsy.

explode   explore   exactly

dolphin   alphabet   orphan

passage   bandage   storage

exchange

nephew

packages

Sight word.

Hillingdale's

disappointed

pajamas

customer

Stripes in a Box

Most days, on the way to school, the children would push and giggle and wiggle around until the mother who was driving would say, "Quiet down!"

But now they were so quiet that Mark's mother looked around at them. It was *too* quiet. She thought something was wrong. "Is everything all right?" she asked.

"Sure, Mom," said Mark.

Ronnie picked up two boxes that were on the floor. He shook them. "What's in these boxes?" he asked.

"Just some things my mother has to return to the store," said Mark.

"Here we are," said Mark's mother. They were at school.

"The snake must have wiggled out the window," whispered Ronnie.

"Or out the door," said Jill.

"But how?" said Betsy. "Oh, dear!" She picked up her empty basket and got out of the car.

Mark's mother turned the car around. "I will just have time to return those things to Hillingdale's," she thought. And she looked in back to make sure her packages were there. "There's that dress I decided I don't like and the pajamas that were too big for Mark."

Now how could she know that in one of the boxes was a little gray snake with a yellow neck? She couldn't! So off she drove to Hillingdale's.

First Mark's mother returned her dress. Then she went across the store and said to a saleslady, "I would like to exchange these pajamas, please. They are too big for my boy. I need a size 8."

The saleslady said, "Here is a size 8." Then she turned to another customer who was standing there and said, "I'm sorry, but we are all out of size 10."

The woman said, "Oh, dear," and turned away, disappointed.

"Wait!" said Mark's mother. "I'm returning a size 10. Maybe you would like these."

"Thank you," said the other woman. "Red and white stripes. How nice! I hope my nephew likes red and white stripes. I'm getting these for his birthday."

"Boys like stripes," said the saleslady.

"I'll take them!" said the woman. "Just leave them right in that box."

Now how could she know that in the box was also a little gray snake with a yellow neck? She couldn't!

She paid $3.98, put the box under her arm, and went off to her nephew's house.

We work with words.

fault lawn saucer crawl

honey chimney valley

Sight words.

lettuce dangerous Gladys

Sound the words.

crawled

Barney

gloves

beauty

ring-necked

Paul

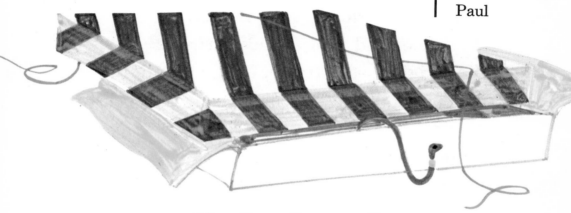

The Best Present Ever

"Happy birthday, Homer dear," said his aunt. She gave Homer a big hug and a kiss and handed him the box. Then she left him with his friends Barney and Paul, who were there to help him celebrate. And she went into the kitchen to talk to Homer's mother.

As Homer opened the box, out crawled the little snake. "A snake!" cried Barney.

189

"It's just what I wanted, Aunt Gladys!" shouted Homer to his aunt.

"Do you really like it?" called his aunt.

"It's a beauty," said Homer, putting the little snake on his arm.

"Is the size all right?" she asked.

"It's just perfect," said Homer.

"Let me hold him," said Barney.

"All right," said Homer. He ran into the kitchen. "It's the best present I ever got!" he said to his aunt.

"I'm glad, Homer," she said, a little surprised. "Well, I have to leave now. Good-by."

"Mother," said Homer, "can I have some lettuce to feed my snake?"

"Your snake?" asked his mother.

"The snake Aunt Gladys gave me," said Homer.

"Aunt Gladys gave you a snake?" cried his mother. "I don't believe it!"

"Hey, Homer," called Paul. "He went under the couch. We can't get him."

Homer's mother ran into the living room and looked under the couch. Just then Homer's father came home.

"Martin," said Homer's mother, "Gladys gave Homer a snake for his birthday!"

"A snake!" said Dad. He looked under the couch. Then he turned to Homer. "Son, did you really get the snake from Aunt Gladys?"

"Yes, Dad," said Homer. "It came from Hillingdale's."

"It must be a mistake," said his father. He went into the bedroom and came back with a pair of gloves. "It might be dangerous," he said. "I'll catch it. When I count to three, you boys pick up the ends of the couch. One. Two. Three."

The boys picked up the couch. Homer's father grabbed the snake and dropped it into a jar.

"Where are you going?" asked Homer's mother.

"I'm going to show it to Jim Belt," said Dad. "He lives down the street. Jim works at the zoo and knows about reptiles. He'll know if this one is dangerous." And he rushed out the door.

"Can I keep him, Mom?" asked Homer. "He's so small. I can keep him in a cage."

"I'm not sure, Homer," said his mother. She looked inside the box. "Well, look at these nice pajamas!"

"They're pretty nice," said Homer. "But I still want the snake."

Before long Homer's father came back. He had taken his gloves off. "It's a ring-necked snake," he said. "And it's harmless. We'll keep it tonight. Tomorrow morning we can let it out in the woods."

"But, Dad, it was a present!" said Homer. "And Mom said maybe I could keep him in a snake cage."

"It's all right with me," his mother said, "if it's harmless. But Homer will have to feed it and take care of it himself."

"I will," said Homer.

"I'm sure it was all a mistake," said his father, "but happy birthday, Homer!"

And he gave Homer back his snake.

We work with words.

favor	beggar	tower
clear	bears	search
herd	squirt	scurry

Sight word.

Nichols

Sound the words.

hammer

early

curled

okay

raisins

Ringer

Raisins and Toast

Later that day, Mark's mother drove back to school to pick up Betsy, Mark, Ronnie, and Jill.

As soon as they were in the car, they began looking around again for the snake.

"Did you find anything in the car today, Mrs. Nichols?" asked Betsy.

"No, Betsy," said Mrs. Nichols. "Why? Did you leave your sweater?"

"No, Mrs. Nichols," said Betsy.

194

"Maybe the snake went into one of those boxes," whispered Ronnie.

"Mom, what's in these boxes?" asked Mark.

"Some things from Hillingdale's," said Mrs. Nichols. "I just got them."

"But the boxes were here this morning," said Ronnie.

"No, those were other boxes," said Mrs. Nichols. "I returned them to Hillingdale's while you were at school. These are different boxes."

"The snake must be at Hillingdale's," sighed Betsy. "That's no place for a snake."

"Maybe he'll get away," said Mark.

"After all, Betsy," said Ronnie. "He got away from us."

"Yes, he did," said Betsy.

Homer kept his birthday snake in the basement. The next morning he got up early and went downstairs in his pajamas. The snake was sleeping. Homer picked up the jar, took off the lid, and dropped in some raisins and toast.

"Hi there, little ring-necked snake," said Homer. "I think I'll call you Ringer!"

Later, at school, Homer sat by Barney. "How's the snake?" Barney whispered.

"Okay," whispered Homer.

"What did you feed him?" asked Barney.

"Raisins and toast," whispered Homer.

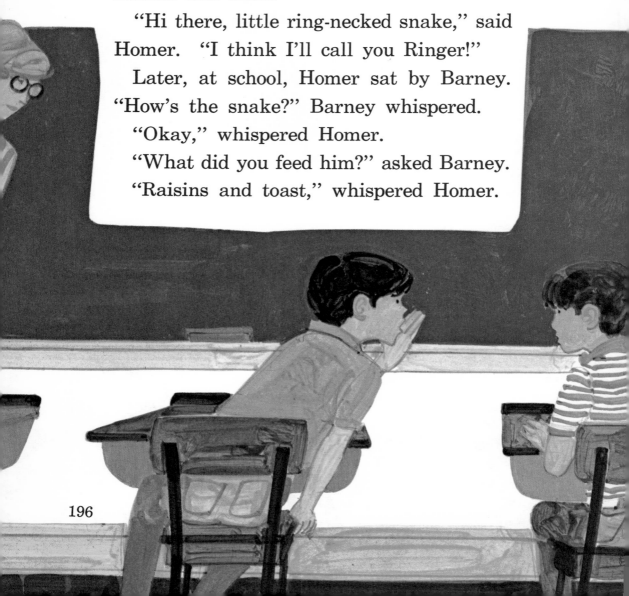

Just then the teacher began asking questions. "Name two things that farmers grow in Ohio, Barney Ferguson."

Barney looked up. "Raisins and toast," he said. The class laughed.

"That's not funny," said the teacher.

"Corn," said Barney. "They grow wheat and corn."

"That's better," said the teacher.

After school, Barney said, "You almost got me into trouble."

"I'm sorry," said Homer. "Are you coming over to my house this afternoon?"

"Okay," said Barney.

"Bring a hammer," said Homer. "I've got to start building a snake cage. Do you want to help me?"

"Sure," said Barney.

"Me, too," said Paul.

They were at Homer's house in five minutes. Each boy had a hammer. They peeked in at the snake.

"He's still sleeping," said Barney.

"He doesn't look well to me," said Paul.

"I think you're making him sick with the raisins and toast," said Barney.

"I don't think he ate any," said Homer.

"That's what I mean," said Barney. "Why don't we go to the library and get a book on snakes and find out what snakes like to eat."

"Good idea," said Homer. "Let's go."

The librarian found them a book called *Snakes, Large and Small.*

"Snakes," said Homer, reading to the others, "eat worms and lizards."

"See," said Barney. "No raisins. No toast."

Now they knew what real snake food was. Every day, after school, they looked for food for the snake. Down by the river and under rocks, they found lizards. In the backyard, they dug for worms.

They would give Ringer his food. Then
they would work on the snake cage. It took
them the rest of the week to build it. By
Friday, it was finished. It was a big wooden
box, with glass on one side. There were
air holes in the top. And on one end there
was a little door that closed with a hook.

Homer dropped Ringer into the cage.
"Home sweet home," he said. And he shut
the door. Ringer curled up and went to
sleep in his new home.

movie   color   shovel   proves

breakfast   greatest   scream   reason

loose   overtook   woolly   bloom   boo

square   careless   scare   bare

fairness   happiness   freshness   goodness

diet   busiest   dial   dialed

punch

whose   Snaky

It's My Snake!

The next morning Homer dropped Ringer into the jar and took him for a walk. There were some girls down the street playing around. "I'll show Ringer to them," thought Homer. "I bet they'll scream."

He went up to a little girl in a red dress. "Look at this," he said. "Boo!" And he stuck the jar in front of her nose.

But the little girl didn't scream. She just grinned. "My goodness," she said. "Where did you find him?" And she took the jar.

Homer was so surprised, he just let her take it. She opened the jar, took Ringer out, and held him right in her hand.

"Hey, what are you doing?" said Homer. "He'll get away."

"I know what I'm doing, because it's my snake," said the girl whose name was Betsy.

"What do you mean, *your* snake?" Homer shouted. "He's mine! I got him for my birthday!" He grabbed for the snake.

"Quiet!" said Betsy. "You'll scare him."

"You just give him to me," said Homer. "He's mine. My Aunt Gladys bought him for me. In Hillingdale's."

"Hillingdale's!" cried Betsy. "That proves he's mine. I caught him, and I took him to school. But he crawled away and got into a Hillingdale's box. See? I bet your aunt didn't *know* he was in the box. Thanks for finding him, anyway."

Betsy started to walk away. Homer tried to get close to Ringer. But there seemed to be girls everywhere, getting in his way.

Homer shouted, "Give me my snake!"

Betsy stopped and turned around. "If you're so sure he's yours," she said, "go ask your aunt."

"All right," said Homer. "I'll call her right now." He walked to his house, and Betsy followed him. He dialed his aunt's number.

"Hello," he said. "Aunt Gladys, I want to ask you about the present you gave me."

"Do they fit?" asked Aunt Gladys.

"Fit?" asked Homer. "What fit?"

"The pajamas," said Aunt Gladys.

"I mean the snake," said Homer.

"Snake!" cried Aunt Gladys. "What snake?"

Betsy stuck her ear next to the phone. She could hear a voice say, "Homer, I know this is a joke. I didn't give you a snake. I gave you pajamas."

"Okay, Aunt Gladys," said Homer. "Good-by now." He hung up sadly. "I guess you're right," he said to Betsy. "But it sounds crazy to me. If he went in the box, why didn't you get him out?" asked Homer.

"Because I didn't know he was in the box," Betsy said, "until it was returned to the store!" Then she looked down at the snake cage. "What's that?" she asked. "Is it his?"

"Yes," said Homer. He gave the cage an angry little kick. "It sure took us a long time to build this thing."

"I'll bet it did," said Betsy. "It's nice."

Betsy picked up the snake and started to walk away. "If I have any questions about Snaky, I'll come and ask you," she said.

"His name is Ringer," said Homer.

Betsy giggled. "Ringer! That's a silly name for a snake."

"It's not silly," said Homer. "He's a ring-necked snake. And maybe you've wondered what he should eat. He eats worms and very small lizards."

"Worms and lizards!" said Betsy. "Where do I get them?"

"I can show you," said Homer. Then he looked down at the cage that Barney and Paul had helped him build. It sure was a beauty! What was he going to do with it now?

Homer looked up from the cage back to the girl. "Hey!" he said. "What's your name?"

"Betsy."

"Mine's Homer. Look, I've got an idea. You found Snaky—I mean Ringer. But I kept him nice and safe and gave him a home, and I know what he likes to eat. Why don't we be partners?"

"Partners?" said Betsy.

"Yes," said Homer. "He can be part mine and part yours. He can live here, because I've got the cage. But you can come and see him and play with him and feed him any time you feel like it. Even when I'm not here! How about that?"

Betsy looked at the snake cage and thought about being partners with Homer. If she took her snake home, she could just see her mother standing there at the door saying, "GET THAT THING OUT OF HERE!"

"It's a good idea," said Betsy. "But—"

"But what?" said Homer.

"Well," said Betsy. "Can I bring my friends from the carpool to see him?"

"Sure," said Homer. "We're partners?"

"Partners!" said Betsy.

Just then Barney and Paul came along.

"Who's this?" asked Barney.

"And what's she doing with Ringer?" Paul asked.

"We're partners," said Homer. And he told them the story.

"Snake partners. Hey, that's funny," said Paul. "Wait a minute. Why can't we be your partners, too?"

"We helped build the cage," said Paul.

Betsy looked at Homer. "It's fine with me," she said.

"Okay," said Homer. "Now give Ringer back to me. He ought to be in the cage."

"I'll put him in," Betsy said. Barney opened the little door. Betsy gently dropped Ringer into the cage.

"She handles him very well," said Barney.

"She caught him with her bare hands," said Homer.

"Do you believe she really caught him with her bare hands?" asked Paul.

"Sure," said Homer. "I can tell."

Betsy stood up. "Hey," she said. "We forgot to shake."

"Shake what?" asked Barney.

"Shake hands!" said Betsy. "That proves we're partners."

"Shake," said Homer.

And they all shook hands.

"I have to go home now," said Betsy. "Good-by. I'll see you later."

"We'll look for food in the morning," said Paul.

Betsy waved. "I'll see you then."

Homer and Barney and Paul watched Betsy as she walked out of the yard.

"Well, we're snake partners," said Homer. He gave Paul a little punch in the arm.

"Crazy way to get a snake," said Paul. And he gave Barney a little punch.

Then they all had a laughing fit and began wrestling, for no good reason at all.

Think about This:

Why was Betsy so sure Ringer was her snake? What made Betsy think that it would be good to have Homer as a partner?

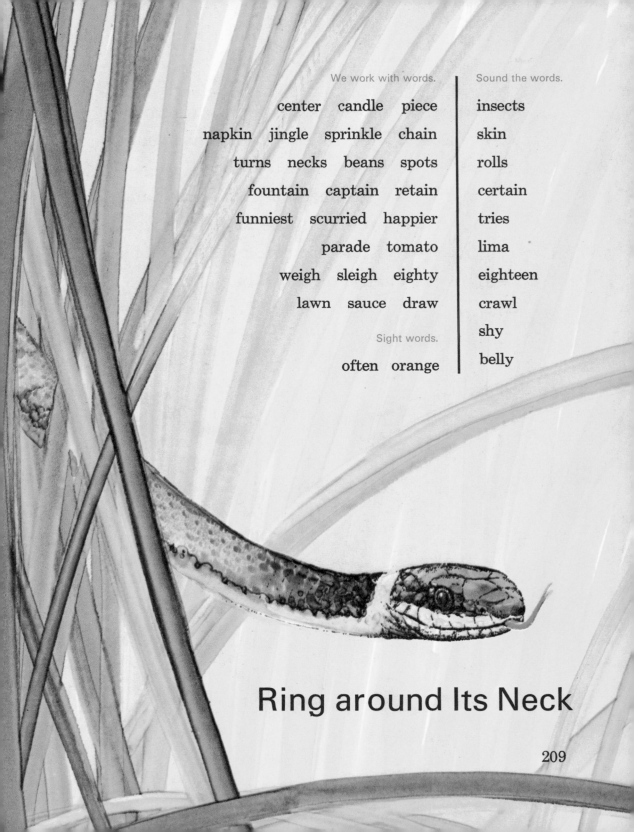

center   candle   piece

insects

napkin   jingle   sprinkle   chain

skin

turns   necks   beans   spots

rolls

fountain   captain   retain

certain

funniest   scurried   happier

tries

parade   tomato

lima

weigh   sleigh   eighty

eighteen

lawn   sauce   draw

crawl

shy

belly

often   orange

Ring around Its Neck

Ring-necked snakes live in many parts of our country. They can be found in almost any woods. They like to live under rocks or under the bark of dead trees.

The ring-necked snake has a gray back and a bright ring around its neck. The bright ring may be yellow or red or orange. The belly of the snake may also be yellow, red, or orange. Sometimes there are black spots on the belly, too.

Many snakes do not lay eggs, but the ring-necked snake does. She lays her eggs in dirt, in dead leaves, or in dead wood. At first the eggs look like white lima beans and are about an inch long. The eggs may take as long as eight weeks to hatch. But if they are in a warm place, they will hatch faster.

When it is time for the eggs to hatch, they no longer look like lima beans. They look more like small, bumpy rocks. At last the baby snakes will poke their heads out of the eggs and look around. Then they will often go right back into the eggs! These little snakes are very shy. They may wait all day before they are brave enough to leave their eggs and crawl away.

211

When the ring-necked snake hatches, it is four or five inches long. But it will grow to be from twelve to eighteen inches long. As the snake grows, it gets too big for its skin. So it grows a new skin under the old one. Then it will crawl right out of its old skin. The old skin rolls off, and it turns inside out as it rolls off. The ring-necked snake will grow many new skins before it becomes eighteen inches long.

The ring-necked snake eats insects, worms, lizards, and other small animals. After a big dinner, the snake may not eat again for days. And when winter comes, the snake can sleep for weeks without eating.

The ring-necked snake is shy and quiet. It sleeps or hides in the daytime and looks for food at night. It tries to get away if someone picks it up. But it seldom tries to bite, and it will soon become tame.

Not many ring-necked snakes are kept as pets. Often they won't eat after they have been caught. Then it's best to let them go. These snakes are a help to man because they eat so many insects.

Some snakes are not safe to pick up. It's best to be certain a snake is safe before going near it. One way to be certain is to get someone who knows about reptiles to look at the snake. Not all snakes are as harmless as the shy ring-necked snake.

Think about This:

Why don't ring-necked snakes make good pets? Find out if all snakes help man.

FE·FI·FO·FUM

We work with words.

breakfast   greatest   dreaming

slate   trade   scurry

spruce   strongest   threw

Sound the words.

grizzly

sly

frozen

quick

Why the Bear Has a Short Tail

One cold day a grizzly bear met a sly fox who came walking along with a string of fish.

"Where did you get those fish?" asked the bear.

"Oh, I've been out fishing, and I caught them," said the fox.

"Where did you go fishing?" asked the grizzly bear.

"Down at the big lake," answered the sly fox. And he started to walk on.

"But the lake is frozen over," said the bear. "It has ice on it. How can you catch fish in a frozen lake?"

"Oh, it's easy," said the fox. "All you have to do is to cut a little round hole in the ice. Then you stick your tail down into the hole. Hold it there as long as you can. The longer you hold your tail there, the more fish you'll catch."

"Then what do I do?" asked the bear.

"Then you give your tail a quick pull," said the fox. "That's all there is to it."

"Oh, that's easy," said the bear.

So the grizzly bear went to the big lake and did just what the sly fox told him to do. His tail began to get cold, but he kept it in the hole.

"I'm going to catch as many fish as I can," he thought to himself. "With my long tail I should catch lots of fish."

Soon the bear was so cold that he began to shake.

"I'll see how many fish I have," the bear said to himself. He gave his tail a quick pull. But it did not come out of the hole. It had frozen in the ice!

Once again the bear pulled very hard. At last his tail came out! But it snapped off short. And that's why the bear has a short tail today.

Or so they say.

Think about This:

What did the bear learn from the fox?
What is another good name for this story?

Turtle's Tug-of-War

Turtle said one day, "I am as smart and as great as Elephant and Hippopotamus. We are the smartest and greatest animals in the land."

The other animals heard him. "What? You, a little turtle, think that you are as smart and as great as Elephant and Hippo? What a laugh! Ha, ha, ha!"

"Wait and see," said Turtle. "I have a plan." And after a while he went off into the woods to search for Elephant.

"Hi, Friend Elephant," said Turtle. "How are you, Brother?"

"You funny little animal," said Elephant. "You think you are as smart and as great as I am. What a laugh! Ha, ha, ha!"

"Wait and see," thought Turtle. "I have a plan." Then he went in search of Hippo. "Hi, Friend Hippo," Turtle said aloud. "How are you, Brother?"

"Why, you funny little animal," said Hippo. "You said you are as smart and as great as I am. What a laugh! Ha, ha, ha!"

"Wait and see," thought Turtle. "I have a plan." Then he said aloud, "Hippo, let's have a tug-of-war. If you cannot pull me over, will you be my friend?"

Hippo laughed and laughed. "If I cannot pull you over, make me into fish food!" he said. "Turtle, we shall have a tug-of-war. If I cannot pull you over, you win. Then we will be friends."

Turtle went back to talk to Elephant next. "Elephant, let's have a tug-of-war," said Turtle. "If you cannot pull me over, I win. Then we can be friends."

Elephant laughed. "If I cannot pull you over in a tug-of-war, make me into fish food!" he said. "If you wish, Turtle, we shall have a tug-of-war."

Then Turtle got a long, thick vine, the longest and strongest he could find.

"Here, Elephant, take the end of this vine," said Turtle. "Hold on to it, and I'll ring a bell when I'm ready to pull."

Turtle took the other end of the thick vine and ran over a hill to Hippo. "Here, Hippo," said Turtle. "This vine is for the tug-of-war. Hold this end of the vine. I'll ring a bell when I'm ready."

Then Turtle ran back a little way so Hippo and Elephant could not see him. He sat down under a tree.

"Get ready!" he called. "One, two, three! Go!" And he rang the bell.

Now Hippo could not see Elephant, and Elephant could not see Hippo. But when Turtle rang the bell, they began the big tug-of-war. Elephant pulled hard, and Hippo pulled hard. They huffed and they puffed. They pulled this way and that way.

And Turtle sat under the tree and laughed and laughed.

At last Turtle thought, "I'm afraid to let them pull any longer. They may find out about my trick."

So he rang the bell and cut the vine. Elephant sat down hard. Hippo sat down hard. Then Turtle took the cut end of the vine to show Hippo.

"Turtle, I didn't pull you over," said Hippo. "You have great strength. I am very tired. We shall be friends."

"Thank you, Brother Hippo," said Turtle, smiling.

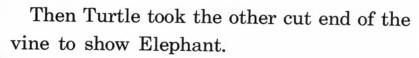

Then Turtle took the other cut end of the vine to show Elephant.

"Turtle," said Elephant, "I didn't know you had so much strength. You win. And we shall be friends."

"Thank you, Brother Elephant," said Turtle, smiling.

And from that day on, Turtle, Hippo, and Elephant have walked together as friends. But Turtle has never wanted to have another tug-of-war!

Sizes

If you were as big as a giant flea,
How much would you have to grow to be
The size of the tiniest head-to-tail
Very most midgety baby whale?

I mean to say—and it's no surprise—
Whatever you do about your size,
There's always something a size or two
Very much bigger or smaller than you.

I mean to say, what's big of some
Is small of others. Now get along home.
And whether you stay or wander far,
Be just the size of whatever you are.

by John Ciardi

We work with words.

sense   rise   worse

charge   dodge   fudge   singe

scold   scurry   scatter

chew   pew   drew

Sight word.

Englishman

Sound the words.

suppose

huge

scurried

threw

breakfast

beanstalk

Jack and the Beanstalk

227

Magic Beans

Once there was a woman who lived with her son, Jack. They were so poor that Jack's mother sent him to sell their only cow.

As Jack led the cow down the road, he met a funny-looking old man.

"Good morning," said the man. "See my magic beans? Give me your cow, and I'll give you five beans."

"Go along," said Jack. "That would be a good trade for you, but not for me."

"Oh!" said the man. "You don't know about these magic beans. Suppose you plant them in your yard today. By tomorrow they will have grown right up to the sky!"

"Really?" said Jack. "Well, that would be a good trade for me." So he gave his cow to the funny-looking old man. Then Jack took the beans home.

"How much did you get for the cow?" asked Jack's mother. When Jack showed her the beans, she became very angry. She threw the beans out the window and sent Jack to bed.

The next morning when Jack woke up, his room looked strange. The sun was shining, but his room was dark. Jack hurried to the window. And what do you suppose he saw?

A huge beanstalk had grown up and up into the sky. Jack could see no end to the tall beanstalk.

"The beans are magic!" cried Jack. "Now I can climb up, up the beanstalk!"

Jack jumped on the big beanstalk. And he climbed and he climbed and he climbed and he climbed until he reached a strange land in the sky. He walked along a road that led to a huge house. Jack was tired, so he stopped at the door. When he knocked, a big tall woman came to the door.

"Would you be so kind as to give me some breakfast?" asked Jack.

"It's breakfast you want, is it?" said the big tall woman. "But it's breakfast you'll be, if you don't scurry away. This is the home of a giant, and he'll eat you if he finds you here. Now, go away!"

"But I've walked a long way," said Jack. "And I'm very tired and hungry."

At last she took Jack into the kitchen
and gave him bread and milk. While Jack
was eating, he heard a loud thump! thump!

"That is the giant!" cried the woman.
"Scurry into the oven. Quick! He must not
see you!"

When the giant came into the room, he
cried, "Fe-fi-fo-fum,

     I smell an Englishman."

Jack was frightened. He kept very quiet
in the oven.

"You're only dreaming," said the wife.
"Come and eat your breakfast." So the giant
sat down and ate breakfast.

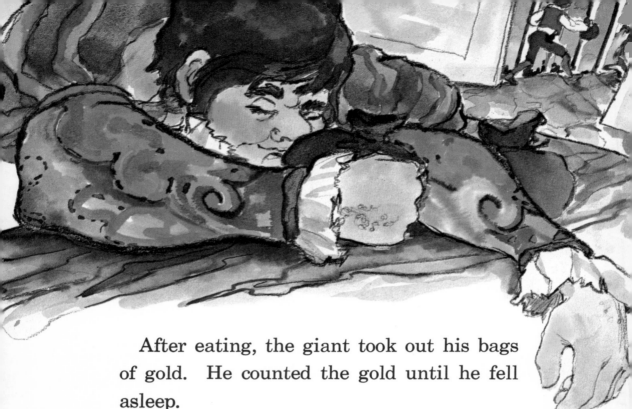

After eating, the giant took out his bags of gold. He counted the gold until he fell asleep.

Then Jack crawled out of the oven and started for the door. On his way out he grabbed one of the bags of gold. Then he scurried down the road to the beanstalk.

Down, down he climbed until he got home. He showed the bag of gold to his mother.

"Well, Mother, I was right about the beans," said Jack. "They are magic!"

As days went by, Jack and his mother used up all the gold. So Jack made up his mind to climb up the beanstalk again.

We work with words

dollar   slippery   ribbon
forest   measure   redraw   careless

Sound the words.

happily
golden
clucked
harp

Magic Gold

Once more Jack jumped on the beanstalk. He climbed and climbed and climbed until he reached the sky. Then he walked along the road that led to the huge house. When Jack knocked on the door, the big tall woman opened it.

"Scurry away, my boy," said the woman. "The giant will eat you if he finds you here!"

"But I've been walking a long way," Jack said. "I'm very hungry and tired."

At last she took Jack into the kitchen and gave him some bread and milk. Before long they heard a loud thump! thump! Again the woman hid Jack in the oven.

When the giant came into the room, he cried, "Fe-fi-fo-fum,

I smell an Englishman."

The wife hurried with breakfast. After the giant finished eating, he said, "Bring me the hen that lays the golden eggs."

Quickly the wife brought the hen. Jack watched from a crack in the oven door. The giant said, "Lay!" to the little hen. And it laid a golden egg. Soon the giant nodded his head and began to snore so loudly that the house shook.

Jack crawled out of the oven and grabbed the golden hen. But the hen clucked and clucked and woke up the giant.

"Wife! Wife!" called the giant. "What have you done with my golden hen?"

That was all Jack heard, for he was running down the road to the beanstalk. When he got home, he showed his mother the wonderful golden hen.

"Lay, hen, lay!" said Jack. And each time Jack told the hen to lay, she laid a golden egg.

Jack made up his mind to climb up the beanstalk one more time. He returned to the giant's house, but this time he did not knock on the door. He slipped into the house and hid in a huge kettle.

Soon he heard a thump! thump! thump! The giant came into the kitchen and cried,

"Fe-fi-fo-fum,

I smell an Englishman."

"If it's the boy who took the golden hen, he's in the oven," said the wife. They both rushed to the oven. But Jack wasn't there. So the giant sat down to eat.

"Wife! Wife! Bring me my golden harp!" called the giant. So the wife brought the harp and put it on the table before him.

"Sing! Sing!" said the giant. The golden harp sang. As it finished, the giant began to snore so loudly that the house shook.

Then Jack climbed out of the kettle and crawled over to the table. He took the harp and ran to the door.

"Help! Help!" cried the harp. The giant woke up just in time to see Jack running away with his golden harp.

Jack ran as fast as he could. But the giant's steps were ten times as long as Jack's.

When Jack got to the beanstalk, he looked back. The giant was not far behind him. Jack was afraid. So down the beanstalk he started. But the huge, angry giant was right behind him.

Jack climbed down and down and down
until he was very close to home. Then he
called, "Mother! Mother! Bring me the ax!"

When Jack reached the ground, he looked
up the beanstalk and saw the giant coming
down very fast. His mother came running
with the ax, and Jack began to chop at the
beanstalk. But the giant was coming closer
and closer. Jack gave one last chop to the
beanstalk. Down it fell with a loud crash!
And that was the end of the giant.

After that, Jack and his mother sold the
golden eggs, played the golden harp, and
lived happily ever after.

The Elves and the Shoemaker

239

Once there was a shoemaker who was very poor. He worked hard, but he could not earn enough money for himself and his wife.

At last the poor shoemaker had nothing left but one strip of leather. It was not a very big strip. He could make only one pair of shoes from it.

"I'll cut out the shoes tonight," the shoemaker told his wife. "Then tomorrow I'll finish them and sell them."

So the shoemaker cut out a pair of shoes and left them on the table. Then he and his wife went to bed.

The next morning the shoemaker and his wife got up early. They ate breakfast. Then the shoemaker went to his table to finish his work. But there stood a pair of shoes. Someone had already finished them!

How surprised the shoemaker was! He did not know what to think. He took the shoes in his hand and looked them over. Then he showed them to his wife.

"These shoes are made well," he said. "Every stitch is in its right place."

Soon a man came in and asked to see some shoes. He was pleased with the pair the shoemaker showed him. He was so pleased that he paid more for them than the poor shoemaker asked.

"Now I have enough money to buy leather for two pairs of shoes," said the happy shoemaker to himself.

That night he cut out the shoes and left them on the table as before.

"I'll finish them in the morning," he told his wife. And they went to bed.

But the next morning he found two pairs of shoes on the table. They were already finished, and every stitch was in place.

Before long another man came in to buy some shoes. He liked the shoes that the shoemaker had. He liked them so well that he took both pairs. And he gave the poor shoemaker enough money to buy leather for four new pairs of shoes.

Again the shoemaker cut out the shoes and left them on his table. By the next day the four pairs were finished. And so it always happened. The leather the shoemaker cut out at night was made into shoes by morning.

Again and again this happened until the shoemaker and his wife were rich.

One night, as the shoemaker cut a strip of leather, he said, "Wife, how would it be if we were to stay up tonight and see who is making the shoes?"

His wife liked the idea, and she lit a candle. Then she and the shoemaker hid in the corner of the room. They hid behind some coats hanging in the corner. Then they began to watch.

Soon two little elves came in without a stitch of clothes on. They sat at the table and went to work making the shoes. How fast they worked! In no time at all the shoes were done, and the elves jumped down and ran away.

The next morning the shoemaker's wife said, "The little elves have made us rich. We can show them how thankful we are by doing something for them. They have no clothes, and they must be cold. I'll tell you what. I'll make them little shirts and coats and pants."

"And I'll make them each a new pair of shoes," said the shoemaker.

So the shoemaker and his wife set to work to make the clothes as a surprise for the little elves.

That night they put the shirts, coats, pants, and shoes on the table. Again they lit a candle and hid in the corner of the room. They wanted to see what the little elves would do.

Before long the two little elves came running into the room. They jumped up on the table to make some shoes. But there was no leather for them to stitch! Then they found the little shirts, coats, pants, and shoes. How pleased they were!

245

The elves quickly took up the new clothes and slipped them on, singing,

"What spruce and dandy boys are we!
No longer shoemakers we will be."

Then they hopped and danced about, jumping over the table and chairs.

At last the little elves danced right out of the door and were never seen again. But from that time on, all went well with the shoemaker and his wife.

Think about This:

Why did the shoemaker and his wife hide after they set out clothes for the elves?

What is another way to end this story?

246

surely easily exactly

lunches fusses wishes

taped skinned folded

handy juicy glassy

twins horses blocks

helpless penniless endless

loudly

riches

wished

fairy

pearls

careless

agree

diamonds

foolish

husband

sausage

Three Wishes

There was once a very poor man who lived with his wife in a little house near a forest. Every day he went into the forest to chop wood.

One day the man said to himself, "Oh, dear, I am so unhappy! I have to work so hard all day long. My wife is hungry, and I am hungry, too. Oh, I am so unhappy!"

Just then he looked up. A beautiful fairy was standing before him.

The fairy said, "My poor man, I heard everything that you said. I am very sorry for you, and I would like to help you. Ask for what you want, and your first three wishes shall be granted."

Then just as suddenly as she had come, the fairy went away.

The man felt very happy now. "I shall go home and tell my wife that a fairy has granted me three wishes," he thought.

He ran back to his house and called to his wife. "Wife! Wife!" he said. "I saw a fairy in the forest, and she said I could have three wishes. I can ask anything I like, and my wishes will be granted! Oh, Wife, I am so happy!"

"I am happy, too," said the woman. "Come, let us go into the house, my dear. Then we can talk about what our wishes will be."

The man went into the little house and sat down at the table. "I am hungry, Wife," he said. "I would like some dinner. While we eat, we can talk about the fairy and the three wishes."

So the man and his wife sat at the table and started to eat their dinner. Then they began to talk about the three wishes.

"We can ask for great riches if we want to," said the man.

"Yes," the wife said. "We can ask for a beautiful house."

"We can even ask for a huge kingdom if we want to," said the man.

And his wife said, "Oh yes, we can ask for pearls and diamonds by the hundred."

"We can ask for a big family," the man added. "I want five boys and five girls."

"I would like six boys and four girls," said the wife.

The man and the woman went on talking like that. But they couldn't agree on the three wishes that would be the best.

The man ate his soup. Then he looked at the dry bread on his plate. "Oh, I wish I had a big sausage for dinner!" he said.

Just then, a great big sausage fell onto the table.

The man was very surprised to see the sausage, and so was his wife.

"Oh, Husband," the wife said. "You have been very careless. You wished for a silly old sausage. Now one of the wishes has been granted. There are only two wishes left."

"I have been careless," said the man. "But we still have two wishes. We can ask for great riches and a kingdom."

"Yes," his wife said. "We can still ask for riches and a kingdom. But we can't ask for ten children, and it's your fault. It's your fault because you asked for a silly sausage."

The poor woman went on fussing. She kept saying over and over again, "It's your fault for being so foolish!"

At last the man said, "I am tired of your fussing! I wish that sausage were hanging from the end of your nose!"

In a second the sausage was hanging from the end of his wife's nose. The poor woman was most surprised, and so was her husband.

The woman started to fuss again, more loudly than before. "Oh, my husband," she said, "you have been very, very foolish! First you asked for a sausage. Then you wished that the sausage were hanging from the end of my nose. That makes two foolish wishes. Now we only have one left!"

"Yes," the man said. "But we can still ask for great riches."

"What good will riches do?" the woman said. "I have a sausage hanging from the end of my nose. It's all your fault!"

The woman started to cry. Then the man said, "Oh, I wish that sausage wasn't here at all!"

All at once the sausage was gone. The man and the woman were right back where they started, as poor as ever. And they had used up all their wishes.

The three wishes had been granted. Still there were no riches, no kingdom, no pearls and diamonds, no little boys, and no little girls.

There wasn't even a sausage for dinner!

ACKNOWLEDGMENTS

Grateful acknowledgment is given for permission to adapt and reprint the following copyrighted material:

"Bookstore Mystery" based upon the story "Mystery In Hawaii" by Charlotte Dowdall, *Three/Four*, August 24, 1969. Copyright © 1969 by Graded Press. Used by permission.

"The Elves and the Shoemaker" adapted from "The Elves" from *Household Stories from the Collection of the Brothers Grimm*. The Macmillan Company.

"Fisherman to Farmer" adapted from "Pepito and His Pets" by Rose Leion. Original version published in the American Red Cross *News;* this adaptation by permission of the author.

"Guess My Line" adapted from "Workers, Here, There and Everywhere." From *Instructor*, ©, Instructor Publications, Inc. Used by permission of the publisher.

"Herbert, the Electrician" adapted from "The Electrical Mouse" by Marie Halun Bloch. *Story Parade*, December 1951. Used by permission of the author.

"Instant Watermelon" from "Homegrown Magic" by Joyce Skaar Butler. Adapted by special permission from *Jack and Jill* Magazine © 1966 The Curtis Publishing Company.

"Jack and the Beanstalk" reprinted by permission of G. P. Putnam's Sons from *English Folk and Fairy Tales* by Joseph Jacobs.

"Mississippi Pete" by Virginia Melchior. From *Child Life*, copyright 1955. Adapted by permission of the publisher.

"Mystery of the Moving Snowman" from "The Mystery of the Traveling Snowman" by Nina Willis Walter. Adapted by special permission from *Jack and Jill* Magazine © 1964 The Curtis Publishing Company.

"Neighbors" adapted from "Communication" by Gertrude W. Pancoast. *Wee Wisdom*, August 1969. Used by permission of the author.

"Oliver, the Elevator Operator" from "The Amazing Adventure of Oliver the Elevator Operator" by C. M. Bryant. Adapted by permission of *Jack and Jill* Magazine. © 1965 The Curtis Publishing Company. All rights reserved.

"Part-Time Dog" adapted from "Randy's Part Time Dog" by Olive Rambo Cook. *Wee Wisdom*, January 1969. Used by permission of the author.

"The River Is a Piece of Sky" from the book *The Reason for the Pelican* by John Ciardi. Copyright, ©, 1959 by John Ciardi. Reprinted by permission of J. B. Lippincott Company.

"Shoeshine Boy" by Jerrold Beim. Reprinted by permission of William Morrow & Company, Inc. Copyright 1954 by Jerrold Beim.

"Shoeshine Song" from *We Live in the City* by Lois Lenski. Copyright, 1954, by Lois Lenski. Published by J. B. Lippincott Company. Reprinted by permission of the author.

255

ILLUSTRATORS

Terry Anderson, Gus Colichidas, Jim Cummins, Vickie Erickson, Tom Hill, David Kerr, Earnie Kollar, Rebecca Lusk, William Mathison, Philip Smith, Al Stine, Joe Szeghy, Judy Thompson, Floyd Webb, Hollis Williford, Darrell Wiskur.

256